LOW CARBS

Important information

All the information, advice and tips in this book were compiled on the basis of current knowledge. However, no responsibility is taken for any information provided. The publisher and authors are not liable for any harm or damage which may result from the practical advice contained in this book. The suggestions contained in this book are not a substitute for examination and treatment by a doctor.

LOW CARBS

CONTENTS

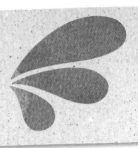

LOW CARBS
The enjoyable way to lose weight

In recent years carbohydrates have come in for a great deal of criticism, mainly because they are said to be responsible for the steady rise in obesity and various illnesses. Pasta, rice, potatoes, bread and rolls define just about every meal, while cakes and pastries are available on every street corner – the entire Western diet is based on carbohydrates as its main source of energy. From a very early age children are given muesli or toast for breakfast, a mid-morning snack of a sandwich at school, pasta or pizza for lunch, and cheese or cold meat with bread for supper. Yet now this is suddenly supposed to be bad for your health?

Carbohydrates represent an important energy source for our bodies. But not all carbohydrates are the same. Short-chain carbohydrates like sugar and white flour are rapidly processed by the body, which means the blood sugar level soars and then drops just as quickly. As a result you feel ravenous! It creates a vicious circle: these carbohydrates increase the desire to eat more and more, which encourages obesity and its associated and secondary diseases such as diabetes, high blood pressure and cardio-vascular conditions.

Long-chain carbohydrates, on the other hand, which are found in fibre and resistant starch, cannot be processed as quickly by the body. They are broken down and released only gradually by the digestive enzymes; as well as preventing peaks and troughs in the blood sugar level, this makes you feel fuller for longer.

The low-carb magic bullet

'Low carb' is now a common abbreviation used to describe food which contains only small amounts of carbohydrates.

People who want to lose weight or improve their health cut down on carbohydrates. If this is your aim, short-chain carbohydrates from white flour and sugar in particular should be cut down and replaced, as these cause fluctuations in blood sugar levels (as explained above) with the associated cravings and risk of obesity. By eating fewer carbohydrates and filling your plate with lean protein and good fat sources, you will be able to fight obesity and lose weight.

The low-carb movement cites human genetics as well as the blood sugar fluctuations caused by short-chain carbohydrates in the argument for reduced carbohydrates in food. The theory is that primitive man had a diet which was low in carbohydrates. Not much fruit was available in summer, so they ate mainly meat rich in protein and fat, mushrooms, and anything else yielded by the forests and fields. So according to this theory human beings are not genetically equipped to deal with the high consumption of carbohydrates, and as a consequence they are getting fatter under the burden of Western cuisine.

To prevent things reaching this stage, carbohydrates in the diet must be reduced, so from now on the watchword is 'low carbs'. A low-carb diet is rich in protein, which gives a satisfying and prolonged feeling of fullness. Snacks between meals are out, calories are saved, and the weight falls off – you feel great and your belly is full. As an added bonus, lots of calories are saved by avoiding or reducing the intake of bread, rolls, pastries and sweet food, so you can see the positive effect on the bathroom scales.

And there is another reason why low carbs are so effective – insulin! This hormone, which is produced naturally in the body, is released when sugar molecules enter the bloodstream. As soon as insulin is present in the blood, fat is no longer broken down because the body's preferred form of energy is sugar. When sugar is no longer present in the blood, the body resorts to the sugar deposits in the form of glycogen in the muscles and liver. Only when the reserves are also exhausted does the body break into the fat deposits, for it is a laborious process for the body to convert fat into a source of energy it can use. So this means that as long as insulin is present in the blood, no matter what the individual does, the fat reserves are blocked off, access denied. The more carbohydrates you eat, the harder it is to get rid of the spare tyres. Even a glass of apple juice after jogging in the afternoon is enough to put the brakes on the fat-burning process. For as soon as sugar is present in the blood, and insulin released, all hope of fat burning is dashed, however sweat-inducing and strenuous your recent run has been.

The Atkins diet

As far back as the 1970s the American cardiologist Dr. Robert Atkins believed that a diet based on meat, fish, eggs and cheese would make the excess pounds drop off. In his opinion, the fat content was not a factor. Food containing carbohydrates was the only item which had to be restricted to small amounts in the diet.

Those who followed the Atkins diet may have lost weight rapidly, but the high fat consumption and lack of carbohydrates can also have negative concomitant effects in the long term, such as cardio-vascular conditions and kidney problems, as well as constipation. The imbalance in this type of diet can result in a deficiency of important nutrients, so it is a potential risk to health and therefore not recommended. Even so, this diet more or less launched the concept of reducing carbohydrates to lose weight.

The low-carb plan

Dr. Atkins allowed for a carbohydrate content of just 15% in his diet plan. Nowadays the amount of carbohydrates recommended tends to be far less extreme. While one current low-carb version allows for a carbohydrate content of 70–120 g per day, another stipulates that it should be less than 40% of the daily energy balance. Yet other variations take account of not only the amount of carbohydrates, but also the speed with which the consumed carbohydrates raise the blood sugar level, as a rocketing blood sugar level is also associated with high insulin release. For instance, the Logi method (a low glycaemic and insulinaemic diet) represents the type of low-carb diet which is very rich in protein and also low in sugar and starch; and another carbohydrate-regulated diet allows for a low-carb meal just in the evening.

The underlying idea is that if you avoid eating carbohydrates in the evening, the body will be forced to begin emptying the carbohydrate store at night and burn fat to produce more energy.

This book is based on a diet with a moderately adjusted carbohydrate intake of below 40% per day (see also section on 'How a low-carb diet works'). This low-carb plan is easily adapted to your everyday life and can be sustained in the long term; weight loss is more successful, as the lower amounts of insulin make it easier to break down fat.

You can certainly survive for a time without any carbohydrates whatsoever, but your health will suffer in the long run. Completely giving up fruit, vegetables, cereals and other sources of carbohydrate is associated with serious nutrient deficiency and an increased risk of cardio-vascular disease. Added to which, few of us could sustain such a strict regime on a permanent basis. So for health and motivational reasons, totally avoiding carbohydrates is not recommended.

Which foods have hidden carbohydrates?

To be able to avoid, or at least reduce, carbohydrates you have to know first in which foods they are found, and in some cases hidden. As a rough guide, everything with sugar, starch or cereal contains carbohydrates. This inevitably excludes many snacks, favourite foods and popular accompaniments. Bread, rolls, cakes, pastries, pasta, potatoes, rice, flour, chips, pizza and kebabs … all of these are now forbidden in larger quantities.

Low-carb compatible

- meat
- fish
- natural milk products
- natural soy products
- wheat gluten (seitan)
- eggs
- nuts and seeds
- oil
- green vegetables

Low-carb incompatible

- food containing sugar
- food containing starch
- cereal-based foods
- baked goods

What is suitable for the low-carb diet?

Two simple rules of thumb will guide you through the carbohydrate maze: avoid eating too many carbohydrates from sugar, starch, cereal, and baked goods. Instead go for meat, fish, natural milk products, natural soy products, wheat gluten, eggs, nuts and seeds, oil, and green vegetables like French beans, cucumber or Swiss chard.

So does this mean you are never allowed to eat an ice cream or sandwich again? Don't worry – this would actually be counterproductive, as all that happens with such strict rules is that you get cravings for the forbidden item. That said, think about how often carbohydrates appear on your plate. Bread and muesli for breakfast? Then a snack of a banana or bar of chocolate? A quick pizza in the evening? This is precisely where you can make a start!

Most types of fruit, however, also contain loads of carbohydrates in the form of fructose. Watch out for hidden carbohydrates in places you would not expect them, namely in ketchup, fruit yoghurt, plant-based milks (soy, oat, rice and almond milks), ready-made sauces, pickled red cabbage, balsamic vinegar, and much more.

How a low-carb diet works

Carry out a spring clean of your old eating habits, stop eating as many carbohydrates, and treat your body instead to good protein sources. For a change, why don't you try an omelette for breakfast or a steak with green salad for your evening meal? And instead of a roll and jam, have half a roll with cheese or herb quark.

As already indicated in the "low-carb plan" section above, the proportion of carbohydrates in your meals should be less than 40% per day, i.e. a maximum of 40% of your daily calories should come from carbohydrates (the rest from fats and proteins).

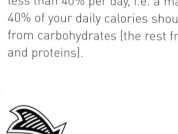

Low-carb rules

- less than 40% carbohydrate per day
- make sure you eat good fats
- protein with every meal
- plenty of salad and green vegetables
- nuts and seeds on a regular basis

Each gram of carbohydrate contains approximately 4 kcal. This means that carbohydrates should make up 120 g in a total calorie intake of 1200 kcal per day, for example, and the recommended amount of carbohydrate in a total calorie intake of 1800 kcal per day would be 180 g.

It goes without saying that you are allowed to enjoy the occasional dessert which is rich in carbohydrates. To balance it out, simply eat something for your other meals which contain few if any carbohydrates, e.g. fried egg with fish or meat. The easiest way to keep a handle on it is to monitor each meal to ensure that the carbohydrate content is less than 40%.

If you want to lose weight, make sure you eat food which is rich in protein and be aware of your fat intake. Proteins make you feel full for a long time, so they should be a standard part of every meal. When it comes to fats, be sure to eat as many 'good' fats as possible, that is, polyunsaturated fatty acids. In practice that means olive or rapeseed oil, for instance, instead of butter, or avocado rather than ham or Gouda in a salad.

For the new food types to become a routine part of your modified diet quickly, it is best not to waste too much time thinking about what you are no longer allowed, and concentrate instead on looking forward to what will appear on your plate. For with the right recipes, the low-carb way can actually be a lot of culinary fun as well.

Foods low in carbohydrate

Meat	Pork, beef, lamb, poultry, game, sausage products (organic)
Fish	Salmon (Pacific), herring (Atlantic), cod (Baltic) and other sustainably caught fish
Vegetables and salad	Cauliflower, spinach, green beans, aubergines, sauerkraut, asparagus, cucumbers, tomatoes, courgettes, white cabbage, Savoy cabbage, onions, rhubarb, lamb's lettuce, leaf lettuce
Fruit	Papaya, blackberries, raspberries, lemons, avocado
Nuts and seeds	Flaxseeds, pecan nuts, pistachios, Brazil nuts, almonds, macadamia nuts, coconut, poppy seeds
Milk & milk products	Cow's milk, sheep's milk, soy milk (unsweetened), buttermilk (natural), kefir (natural), yoghurt (natural), crème fraîche, cream, sour cream, feta, cream cheese, hard cheese, soft cheese, mascarpone, ricotta, quark
Soy products	Tofu (natural), smoked tofu, wheat gluten (natural), soy meat strips
Eggs	

In the "Snacks" chapter you will find a wide range of recipes for crispy kale, vegetable spaghetti, and many other accompaniments which share the same feature: they are so tasty that you won't pine for very long for the traditional filling side dishes.

You will realise that following a low-carb diet over a period of time makes you more creative and inventive by the day. And after a time it will seem quite normal if a meal does not necessarily contain one of the well-known accompaniments.

Accompaniments

For many people, side dishes are an integral part of a complete meal. Favourite Western accompaniments are potatoes, croquettes, chips, rice and pasta. Couscous, millet and bulgur wheat are more unusual examples. But they all have one thing in common: they should no longer fill the plate in a low-carb diet. Pasta and potatoes can still be eaten, of course, just not in large quantities any more. So we need to find a substitute, and that can taste great too! Why don't you try making spaghetti from vegetables like courgettes or squash? And delicious crisps and chips can be made from other vegetables instead of potatoes. Cauliflower and celeriac make excellent substitutes for potatoes in mash and croquettes, and nut flour (e.g. almond or coconut) is great in place of white flour.

Feeling peckish

One thing's for sure: sooner or later you will be overcome with a craving for snacks, whether sweet or savoury. Contrary to all the advertising assurances, rice pudding is not the ideal solution if you feel peckish. It has no place in a low-carb regime, nor is it a proper snack in the context of a healthy, balanced diet. Snacks tend in any case to be very high in carbohydrates: (filled) rolls, muesli bars, crisps, gummi bears, biscuits and cakes, and even healthy options like a piece of fruit or a fruit yoghurt.

You have to think creatively of quick snacks you can eat as part of a low-carb diet. For that peckish feeling usually comes unexpectedly and suddenly—on the go, or in the office—and most of the items you can buy on the fly are not low-carb compatible. So you should prepare yourself in advance, which is not that difficult, as the following list shows.

Suitable snacks

- small portion of tomato and mozza-rella salad
- small portion of tomato, feta and cucumber salad
- hard-boiled egg
- almonds, pistachios, pecan, Brazil or macadamia nuts
- piece of cheese on its own or on a rice cake (plain) with butter and lamb's lettuce
- buttermilk, yoghurt or quark (all natural) with 50 g raspberries or blackberries
- 1–2 small meat or soy sausages
- ½ cucumber to dip in herb quark
- pepper stuffed with cottage cheese
- meatballs without flour
- vegetable bouillon
- ripe avocado to eat with a spoon, with salt and pepper
- 1–2 slices cold roast meat
- grilled aubergine rolls stuffed with soft goat's cheese

Eating out

The canteen is awash with pasta, a business lunch is usually in an Italian restaurant, a candlelit dinner for two means upmarket Asian, and it's a pub lunch with friends on Sundays – carbs lurk on every menu outside your own kitchen. And even in fast food to go, whether sandwiches, kebabs, or burgers, all are packed with carbohydrates. There is only one thing for it – say goodbye to the burger van, sandwiches and chips.

If you are on the move all the time, and therefore eat out a lot, it is certainly harder to follow a low-carb diet. But with some preparation and advance planning, even this challenge can usually be overcome without too much difficulty. If you commit

the following approach to memory and take it on board wholeheartedly, you will already be well ahead of the game: look for a dish containing meat, fish, poultry or tofu and pass on accompaniments like bread, potatoes, chips, rice or pasta, or replace them instead with green vegetables, mushrooms or green salad. Remember to order a sugar-free drink, ideally water. This can be described more specifically as follows.

Quick snacks

Instead of heading for the bakery around the corner, your new destination should be the butcher, the fish shop, or the nearest supermarket. Foods that are low-carb compatible are:

- meat with green leafy salad or cabbage, e.g. meat loaf with green salad or smoked pork chop with pickled cabbage

- feta or ham salad

- marinated Mediterranean vegetables (mushrooms, courgettes, aubergines)

- fried, steamed or grilled fish (no breadcrumbs) with salad or vegetables on the side

- sausages with mustard (no ketchup, chips or bread rolls)

- doner kebab meat (without flatbread and chips)

- meat or fish with salad or side vegetables

Asian

When choosing from an Asian menu, go for crispy fried duck breast instead of rice and spring rolls, for instance. Other suitable choices are:

- meat, fish and tofu dishes with side vegetables, but no rice or noodles
- clear soup containing meat, but no won tons or noodles
- chicken on skewers with sauce

Home cooking

Potato dumplings are out, but chicken halves or roast meat are in. Other low-carb dishes to fill you up are:

- meat and fish with side vegetables or salad
- salad with chicken goujons, feta or ham
- clear bouillon, e.g. with egg garnish
- omelette or fried egg with sausage, and a side salad

We hope you will have fun with our varied selection of low-carb compatible recipes!

Italian

Say "arrivederci" to pizza and pasta. Fortunately, however, there are still plenty of delicious alternatives in this popular Mediterranean cuisine:

- tomato and mozzarella salad
- vitello tonnato (cold sliced veal in creamy tuna sauce)
- antipasti platter, e.g. with ham, Parmesan, chargrilled vegetables, mozzarella, olives
- carpaccio

SALADS

freshness boost

BEETROOT

BATAVIA

RADICCHIO

PEPPER

AVOCADO

BROCCOLI AND CAULIFLOWER
with chorizo

Serves 4
1 head of broccoli
1 small cauliflower
salt
1 red onion
½ garlic clove
½ red chilli
250 g chorizo
coconut oil for frying
2 tbsp red wine vinegar
pepper

Preparation time:
approx. 25 minutes
Per portion:
approx. 347 kcal/1453 kJ
13 g P, 29 g F, 8 g CH

■ Wash and trim the broccoli and cauliflower, and break them into florets. Peel and chop the stalks. Blanch the vegetables in boiling salted water for about 2 minutes and drain well.

■ Peel and dice the onion. Peel and finely slice the garlic. Wash the chilli, pat dry, cut in half lengthways, remove the seeds, membranes and stem ends, and dice the flesh very finely. Slice the chorizo.

■ Heat the coconut oil in a pan and fry the onion, garlic, chilli and chorizo on a medium heat until pale golden, stirring occasionally. De-glaze with the vinegar. Add the blanched vegetables and fry them briefly as well. Season to taste with salt and pepper.

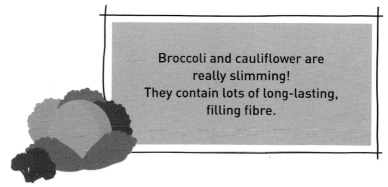

Broccoli and cauliflower are really slimming!
They contain lots of long-lasting, filling fibre.

SUPERFOOD
tabbouleh

Serves 4

6 spring onions

200 g flat-leaf parsley

100 g mint

½ avocado

100 g baby leaf spinach

4 medium tomatoes

juice of 1 unwaxed lemon

2 tbsp olive oil

salt

pepper

50 g pistachios

2 tbsp chia seeds

15 g dried goji berries

■ Wash, trim and finely chop the spring onions. Wash the parsley and mint, shake them dry, and coarsely chop the leaves.

■ Cut the avocado in half and remove the stone; carefully scoop out the flesh and dice it. Wash and pick over the spinach, then shake it dry. Wash, trim, halve and dice the tomatoes.

■ In a large bowl, combine the olive oil, lemon juice, salt and pepper. Add all the prepared ingredients, along with the pistachios, chia seeds and goji berries. Mix well and season to taste. Leave the salad for about 15 minutes for the flavours to develop, then serve.

Preparation time:
approx. 15 minutes
(plus marinating time)
Per portion:
approx. 238 kcal/999 kJ
9 g P, 16 g F, 13 g CH

AVOCADO AND TOMATO SALAD
with pine nuts

Serves 4
For the dressing:
2 small onions
100 ml red wine vinegar
100 ml olive oil
1 tsp salt
½ tsp pepper

For the salad:
2 tbsp pine nuts
2 avocados
1 tbsp lemon juice
4 tomatoes
1 small red onion
6 radishes
½ bunch fresh basil

Preparation time:
approx. 20 minutes
(plus marinating time)
Per portion:
approx. 340 kcal/1424 kJ
3 g P, 34 g F, 6 g CH

■ For the dressing: Peel and coarsely chop the onions, then whizz them with the vinegar in a food mixer on a low setting (or with a hand blender) until smooth.

■ If using a mixer, gradually drizzle in the oil on a low setting, then season with salt and pepper. If not, put the onion mixture into a bowl and slowly add in the oil, stirring well. Season with salt and pepper.

■ For the salad: Dry-roast the pine nuts in a non-stick pan, then set them to one side. Peel, de-stone and slice the avocados. Drizzle the lemon juice over them to prevent them from turning brown. Wash, dry and coarsely chop the tomatoes. Peel the red onion, cut it in half and slice it into thin rings. Trim, wash and finely slice the radishes.

■ Combine the tomatoes, onion and radishes with the avocados and fold in the dressing. If possible, leave to soak for 20 minutes. Wash the basil, pat dry, and cut it into fine strips. Serve the avocado and tomato salad sprinkled with the toasted pine nuts and basil.

THE SALAD WILL BE HIGHER IN PROTEIN IF YOU ADD FRIED TOFU CUBES.

MIXED SALAD
with turkey breast

Serves 4

For the salad:

2 eggs

1 cos lettuce

1 radicchio

4 plum tomatoes

2 bunches chives

150 g mild blue cheese

1 avocado

2 tbsp lemon juice

8 slices bacon

4 small turkey breasts, 150 g each

salt

pepper

paprika powder

For the dressing:

3 tbsp sunflower oil

3 tbsp olive oil

2½ tbsp red wine vinegar

3 tbsp orange juice

1 tbsp Dijon mustard

salt

pepper

1 pinch sugar

■ Prick the eggs and hard-boil them for about 8 minutes. Rinse under cold water, peel them, and leave to cool. Wash and trim the lettuce and radicchio, spin them dry and tear into bite-size pieces. Wash the tomatoes, pat dry, remove the stem ends, and slice the flesh. Wash the chives, pat dry and finely chop them. Crumble the blue cheese. Peel the avocado, remove the stone, and cut the flesh into thin wedges. Drizzle immediately with the lemon juice.

■ Fry the bacon in a non-stick pan without oil. Wash the turkey breasts, pat dry and cut them in half lengthways. Season with salt, pepper and paprika, and fry them in the bacon fat for about 10 minutes until cooked through. Remove them from the pan and leave to cool. Slice the hard-boiled eggs.

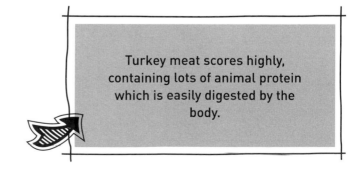

Turkey meat scores highly, containing lots of animal protein which is easily digested by the body.

■ Arrange the salad leaves on 4 plates and spread the sliced tomatoes and eggs on top. Pat the avocado slices dry and add them too, then the crumbled cheese on top. Cut the turkey breasts into bite-size pieces and arrange in overlapping layers on the salad, along with the bacon. Sprinkle with chopped chives.

■ For the dressing: Whisk together the sunflower and olive oils, vinegar, orange juice and mustard.
Season well with salt and pepper and a pinch of sugar.
Drizzle the dressing over the salad with a teaspoon.

Preparation time:
approx. 40 minutes
Per portion:
approx. 670 kcal/2805 kJ
45 g P, 51 g F, 6 g CH

AVOCADO SALAD
with bacon

Serves 4

8 eggs

6 slices bacon

2 small avocados

1 garlic clove

salt

100 g cherry tomatoes

4 spring onions

pepper

Preparation time:
approx. 25 minutes
Per portion:
approx. 439 kcal/1838 kJ
21 g P, 37 g F, 5 g CH

■ Hard-boil the eggs. Leave them to cool, peel, and then chill them in the fridge. Meanwhile dry-fry the bacon in a non-stick pan until crispy, then break it into small pieces. Peel the avocados and remove the stones.

■ In a bowl, use a fork to mash together the avocado flesh, eggs, crushed garlic, and half a teaspoon of salt, combining it all well. Wash the tomatoes and cut them in half; wash and chop the spring onions.

■ Add the tomatoes, spring onions and bacon to the egg mixture and stir well. Season to taste with salt and pepper.

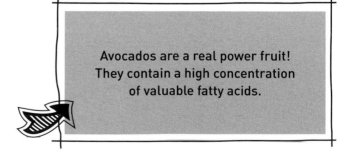

**Avocados are a real power fruit!
They contain a high concentration
of valuable fatty acids.**

GREEK SALAD
with vegetable pasta

Preparation time:
approx. 25 minutes
Per portion:
approx. 264 kcal/1106 kJ
10 g P, 20 g F, 9 g CH

■ Finely dice the sheep's cheese. Wash, dry, trim and quarter the tomatoes. Wash the mint, shake it dry, and finely chop the leaves. Peel the onions and cucumbers, cutting off the ends. Wash and trim the radishes.

■ Using a spiraliser, cut the onions and radishes into thin spaghetti. Cut the cucumbers into broad ribbon noodles, then cut them into smaller pieces.

■ For the dressing: Whisk together all the ingredients with 4 tablespoons of water. Season with salt and pepper.

■ Arrange the cucumber pasta on plates, spread the cheese and tomatoes on top, and garnish with the radish and onion strips. Sprinkle the mint on top, drizzle the dressing over, and serve.

Serves 4

For the salad:

200 g sheep's cheese (e.g. feta)

100 g cherry tomatoes

4 sprigs mint

2 red onions

2 cucumbers

1 bunch radishes

For the dressing:

3 tbsp olive oil

2 tbsp balsamic vinegar

1 tbsp Dijon mustard

1 tbsp honey

salt

pepper

A NEW TAKE ON THIS GREEK CLASSIC

GREEN SALAD
with ranch dressing

Serves 4
For the dressing:
100 g mayonnaise
1 pinch garlic powder
1 pinch onion powder
1 pinch salt
¼ tsp pepper
1 tbsp curly parsley,
  finely chopped
100 ml milk

For the salad:
1 iceberg lettuce
1 small radicchio
1 bunch rocket leaves
4 spring onions
60 g salad cress

Preparation time:
approx. 20 minutes
Per portion:
approx. 250 kcal/1047 kJ
3 g P, 24 g F, 4 g CH

■ For the dressing: Put all the ingredients in a bowl and whisk well.

■ Trim the lettuces and cut or tear them into bite-size pieces. Then wash and spin them dry.

■ Wash, trim and finely chop the spring onions. Add them to the lettuce leaves and combine it all with the ranch dressing. Serve garnished with cress.

IF YOU LIKE, SERVE THE SALAD WITH PROTEIN-RICH FILLET STEAK STRIPS.

BEETROOT AND BROCCOLI SALAD
with chicken

Serves 4

400 g broccoli

salt

5 tbsp olive oil

4 chicken breasts, skin removed (each approx. 200 g)

pepper

1 red onion

2 beetroots

100 g baby spinach

1 bunch basil

1 avocado

1 garlic clove

25 g walnut halves

juice and zest of 1 unwaxed lemon

½ tsp honey

½ tsp Dijon mustard

2 tbsp sesame seeds

■ Wash and trim the broccoli, breaking it into florets. Bring a large pan of salted water to the boil. Blanch the broccoli florets for 2 minutes, then rinse under cold water and drain well. Heat 1 tablespoon of olive oil in a pan and fry the broccoli florets all over until they begin to brown. Lift them out onto a plate and leave to cool.

■ Wash the chicken, pat dry, and season with salt and pepper. Peel the red onion and cut it in half and then into thin rings. Put 1 tablespoon of olive oil into the hot frying pan and brown the chicken breasts on both sides for approximately 4 minutes until cooked. After 3 minutes, add the chopped onion and fry it with the chicken. Set to one side to cool, then cut the chicken into bite-size pieces.

■ Wash and peel the beetroots (ideally wearing disposable plastic gloves), then grate them coarsely. Wash the spinach, pick it over, and spin dry.

■ For the avocado purée: Wash the basil, shake it dry, and tear off the leaves. Save a few leaves for the garnish and put the rest in a food mixer. Cut the avocado in half, remove the stone, and scoop out the flesh. Peel the garlic clove and put it in the mixer containing the basil, along with the avocado, walnut halves, 1 tablespoon of oil, 1 tablespoon of lemon juice, 2–3 tablespoons of cold water, salt, and pepper. Whizz it all until smooth and creamy (or you can use a hand blender for this).

■ For the dressing: Combine the rest of the lemon juice with the honey and mustard, then season with salt and pepper. Stir in the rest of the olive oil.

■ In a large bowl, combine the broccoli and spinach with the dressing, then divide it between four plates. Put the beetroots on top, then arrange the chicken pieces and onion over it.

■ Dry-roast the sesame seeds in a pan. Combine them with the lemon zest and sprinkle over the salad. Spoon a dollop of avocado purée onto each plate alongside the salad, and serve.

Preparation time:
approx. 30 minutes
(plus cooking time)
Per portion:
approx. 522 kcal/2185 kJ
54 g P, 26 g F, 17 g CH

SOUPS

A hot favourite

CAULIFLOWER

HERBS

CHILLIES

COURGETTES

BROCCOLI

GAZPACHO
chilled vegetable soup

Serves 4

2 red peppers

1 mild red chilli

1 cucumber

1 garlic clove

300 g tomatoes

1 tbsp tomato purée

6 tbsp olive oil

salt

pepper

1 tbsp lemon juice

1 sprig mint

Preparation time:
approx. 20 minutes
Per portion:
approx. 180 kcal/754 kJ
2 g P, 15 g F, 7 g CH

■ Wash the peppers and chilli, pat dry, and cut them in half lengthways; remove the seeds, membranes and stem ends. Peel the cucumber, cut it in half lengthways, and scoop out the seeds. Peel the garlic clove. Trim and wash the tomatoes.

■ Coarsely dice the tomatoes, half of the peppers, a third of the cucumber, half of the chilli and the garlic clove. Whizz them all in a food mixer along with the tomato purée and 4 tablespoons of olive oil until smooth. Thin the mixture with a little cold water if necessary, and season with salt, pepper and lemon juice.

■ For the garnish: Finely dice the rest of the peppers, chilli and cucumber. Wash the mint, shake it dry, and pick off the leaves.

■ Whizz the soup briefly again before serving, sprinkle on the chopped vegetables and mint leaves, and drizzle with the remaining olive oil.

SUPER FRESH!

PERFECT FOR COLD WINTER'S DAYS!

ROOT VEGETABLE SOUP
with Brussels sprouts

Serves 4

1 small carrot
2 small parsnips
100 g celeriac
½ leek
100 g Brussels sprouts
1 bunch flat-leaf parsley
6 tbsp oil
2 tbsp butter
1 litre vegetable stock
250 ml cream
2 tbsp sour cream
freshly grated nutmeg
salt
pepper

Preparation time:
approx. 45 minutes
Per portion:
approx. 410 kcal/1717 kJ
5 g P, 40 g F, 8 g CH

■ Peel the carrot, parsnips and celeriac and cut them into thick chunks. Trim the leek, cut it in half lengthways and then into strips, and wash well. Trim and quarter the Brussels sprouts, then cook them in boiling salted water until *al dente*. Strain them in a sieve, rinse under cold water, and leave to drain.

■ Remove the parsley stalks, and fry the leaves in a pan with 5 tablespoons of oil until crispy. Scoop them out of the pan and drain on kitchen paper. Heat 1 tablespoon of butter and the rest of the oil in a pot. Add the carrot, celeriac and leek, and sweat them for a few minutes.

■ De-glaze with the vegetable stock. Bring to the boil and simmer for about 20 minutes on a medium heat. Whizz the soup with a hand blender until smooth and creamy. Add the cream, and simmer for another 5 minutes. Season with salt and pepper.

■ Melt the remaining butter in a pan, and fry the sprouts. Season with a little nutmeg, salt and pepper. Ladle the soup into bowls and arrange the fried sprouts on top. Add a dollop of sour cream and sprinkle with the crispy parsley.

CAULIFLOWER SOUP
with sweetcorn

WITH
COCONUT

approx. 20 minutes
(plus cooking time)
Per portion:
approx. 134 kcal/561 kJ
7 g P, 12 g F, 6 g CH

■ Trim the spring onions, peel the garlic cloves, and slice them all. Heat the olive oil in a pan and fry the spring onions, garlic, and sweetcorn. Season with salt and chilli flakes.

■ Bring the vegetable stock to a boil with the cauliflower and cook uncovered for 10 minutes. Add the coconut milk and whizz with a hand blender until smooth and creamy. Season with salt and lime juice.

■ Remove the coriander stalks; wash the leaves and pat them dry. Stir them through the sweetcorn mixture and spoon it over the soup.

Serves 4
2 spring onions
3 garlic cloves
2 tbsp olive oil
100 g sweetcorn (tin)
salt
chilli flakes
400 g cauliflower florets (frozen)
600 ml vegetable stock
200 ml coconut milk
2 tsp lime juice
2 sprigs coriander

Cauliflower scores points for lots of long-lasting, filling fibre and few calories!

SWISS CHARD SOUP
with tofu

Serves 4

1 kg Swiss chard

5 garlic cloves

1 piece fresh turmeric
  (approx. 1 cm)

1 chilli

1 lemon

200 g silken tofu

2 tbsp olive oil

750 ml vegetable stock

sea salt

Preparation time:
approx. 35 minutes
Per portion:
approx. 180 kcal/754 kJ
10 g P, 13 g F, 5 g CH

■ Wash and trim the chard, and shake it dry. Remove the stalks and dice them very finely. Cut the leaves into strips. Peel the garlic and shave it very finely. Peel the turmeric and chop it very finely. Wash the chilli, remove the seeds, and chop it very finely. Squeeze the juice from the lemon. Drain and dice the tofu.

■ Heat the oil in a pan and fry the garlic. Add the chopped chard stalks and cook until soft, stirring occasionally. Add the chard leaves, turmeric and chilli and sweat them briefly. De-glaze with the stock and lemon juice.

■ Bring it all to the boil and cook for 5 minutes. Add the tofu and heat it up in the soup briefly. Season with salt.

THAI CURRY SOUP
with chicken

Serves 4

1 piece fresh root ginger
  (approx. 2 cm)

2 garlic cloves

2 lemongrass stalks

150 g shiitake mushrooms

300 g carrots

200 g cherry tomatoes

400 g chicken breast fillet

4 tbsp coconut oil

4 tsp red Thai curry paste

400 ml unsweetened
  coconut milk

500 ml vegetable stock

salt

pepper

Preparation time:
approx. 25 minutes
Per portion:
approx. 321 kcal/1344 kJ
25 g P, 18 g F, 15 g CH

■ Peel and finely chop the ginger and garlic. Wash the lemongrass, cut it into long pieces, and beat it flat with a pot. Trim the mushrooms, cutting larger ones in half. Peel the carrots and cut them into thin strips. Wash the tomatoes and cut them in half. Cut the chicken breasts into ½ cm slices.

■ Heat the coconut oil gently until it becomes liquid and mix half of it with the curry paste. Rub this into the chicken pieces.

■ Fry the chicken all over for 2 minutes in the remaining oil, then scoop the pieces out of the pot. Put the ginger, garlic, lemongrass, mushrooms and carrots into the pot and sweat for 2 minutes, stirring all the time. Add the coconut milk and stock and bring to the boil. Add the chicken and tomatoes and cook the soup for another 2 minutes on a medium heat. Season with salt and pepper.

WONDERFULLY
EXOTIC

CHICKEN SOUP
with mushrooms

Serves 4

1 onion

2 garlic cloves

1 red chilli

1 green chilli

1 lemongrass stalk

1 piece fresh galangal root
(approx. 1 cm)

2 tsp red curry paste

1 tbsp groundnut oil

3 kaffir lime leaves

500 ml chicken stock

300 ml coconut milk

250 ml cream

some fish sauce
(e.g. nam pla)

some lime juice

600 g chicken breast fillet

125 g button mushrooms

2 tomatoes

3 spring onions

some fresh coriander
leaves

■ Peel and finely chop the onion and garlic. Wash and trim the chillies, cut them in half, remove the seeds and stem ends, and chop finely. Wash, trim and finely chop the lemongrass. Peel the galangal and chop it finely as well.

■ Fry the spices and curry paste in the groundnut oil. Add the washed lime leaves and chicken stock, and simmer for 15 minutes. Stir in the coconut milk and cream, and simmer for another 5 minutes. Season to taste with fish sauce and lime juice.

■ Meanwhile wash the chicken breasts, pat dry, and cut into strips. Brush the mushrooms clean and slice them. Cover the tomatoes with boiling water for a few minutes, remove the skins and seeds, and dice the flesh finely. Wash, trim and chop the spring onions.

■ Add all of these ingredients to the spicy broth and cook for 5 minutes. Wash the coriander leaves, shake dry, and remove the stalks. Serve the chicken soup sprinkled with coriander leaves.

Preparation time:
approx. 40 minutes
Per portion:
approx. 390 kcal/1633 kJ
40 g P, 22 g F, 10 g CH

GOULASH SOUP
with sauerkraut

Serves 4

200 g beef (e.g. shoulder or braising steak)

1 onion

1 garlic clove

2 tbsp lard

2 tbsp tomato purée

500 ml beef stock

1 tsp cinnamon

1 tbsp paprika

salt

pepper

1 pinch cumin powder

1 tsp dried marjoram

1 green pepper

250 g fresh sauerkraut

2 tsp caraway seeds

Preparation time:
approx. 25 minutes
(plus cooking time)
Per portion:
approx. 303 kcal/1269 kJ
23 g P, 21 g F, 6 g CH

■ Wash the beef, pat dry, and cut it into bite-size chunks. Peel and dice the onion and garlic.

■ Heat the lard in a large pot on a medium setting and sear the meat all over for 10 minutes, stirring frequently.

■ Add the onion and garlic and fry them with the meat for about 5 minutes. Stir in the tomato purée, sweat briefly, and turn the heat down a bit. De-glaze with the stock, season with cinnamon, paprika, salt, pepper, cumin, and marjoram, cover the pot and simmer for about 40 minutes.

■ Wash the pepper, pat dry, and cut it in half lengthways; remove the seeds, membranes and stem end. Dice the pepper, and add it to the soup along with the sauerkraut and caraway seeds. Simmer for another 15 minutes.

CONTAINING ONLY
25 KCAL PER 100 G,
SAUERKRAUT IS GREAT FOR
STAVING OFF
HUNGER PANGS.

SPINACH SOUP
with egg strips

Serves 4
500 g fresh spinach
2 shallots
1–2 garlic cloves
50 g butter
2 tbsp plain flour
800 ml vegetable stock
200 g crème fraîche
salt
pepper
freshly grated nutmeg
1 tbsp oil
2 eggs
100 g diced ham (optional)

Preparation time:
approx. 15 minutes
(plus cooking time)
Per portion:
approx. 451 kcal/1888 kJ
13 g P, 35 g F, 9 g CH

■ Wash the spinach thoroughly, drain, and blanch in boiling water for 1–2 minutes. Strain in a sieve, rinse briefly with cold water, and drain well.

■ Peel and finely chop the shallots and garlic. Melt the butter in a pot, add the shallots and garlic, and sweat for 2–3 minutes. Dust with the flour, stir well, and sweat for another 1–2 minutes.

■ Add the stock and crème fraîche and bring to the boil, stirring all the time. Chop the spinach and add it to the soup. Season with salt, pepper and freshly grated nutmeg.

■ Heat the oil in a pan, beat the eggs, and pour them into the pan. Sprinkle on some salt and pepper, and fry on a medium heat for about 3–5 minutes on each side. Take the eggs out of the pan and cut them into strips.

■ Ladle the spinach soup into bowls and add the egg strips. Sprinkle on some diced ham (optional).

MEAT
Animal magic

GARLIC

CHICKEN

CHILLIES

STEAK

HERBS

BEEF STEAKS
with courgettes

Serves 4
For the gremolata:
50 g parsley
2 unwaxed lemons
2 garlic cloves
salt
pepper

For the steaks:
4 beef steaks
(each approx. 180 g)
4 tbsp olive oil

For the vegetables:
3 courgettes
2 tbsp olive oil
200 g sheep's cheese

Preparation time:
approx. 30 minutes
Per portion:
approx. 560 kcal/2345 kJ
52 g P, 36 g F, 6 g CH

■ For the gremolata: Wash the parsley, shake it dry, remove the stalks, and finely chop the leaves. Wash the lemons in hot water and grate the zest. Peel and finely chop the garlic. Combine these ingredients and season with salt and pepper.

■ Wash the steaks, pat them dry, and press them down slightly. Rub them all over with the gremolata and leave to marinate briefly. Heat the olive oil in a pan and sear the steaks on each side for 2–3 minutes, depending on how well you want the meat to be done. Wrap in foil and leave to rest for 5 minutes.

■ Meanwhile wash, trim and slice the courgettes. Heat the olive oil left in the pan and fry the courgettes briefly, seasoning with salt and pepper. Put the vegetables in a bowl and crumble the sheep's cheese on top. Slice the beef steaks and serve with the courgettes and sheep's cheese on the side.

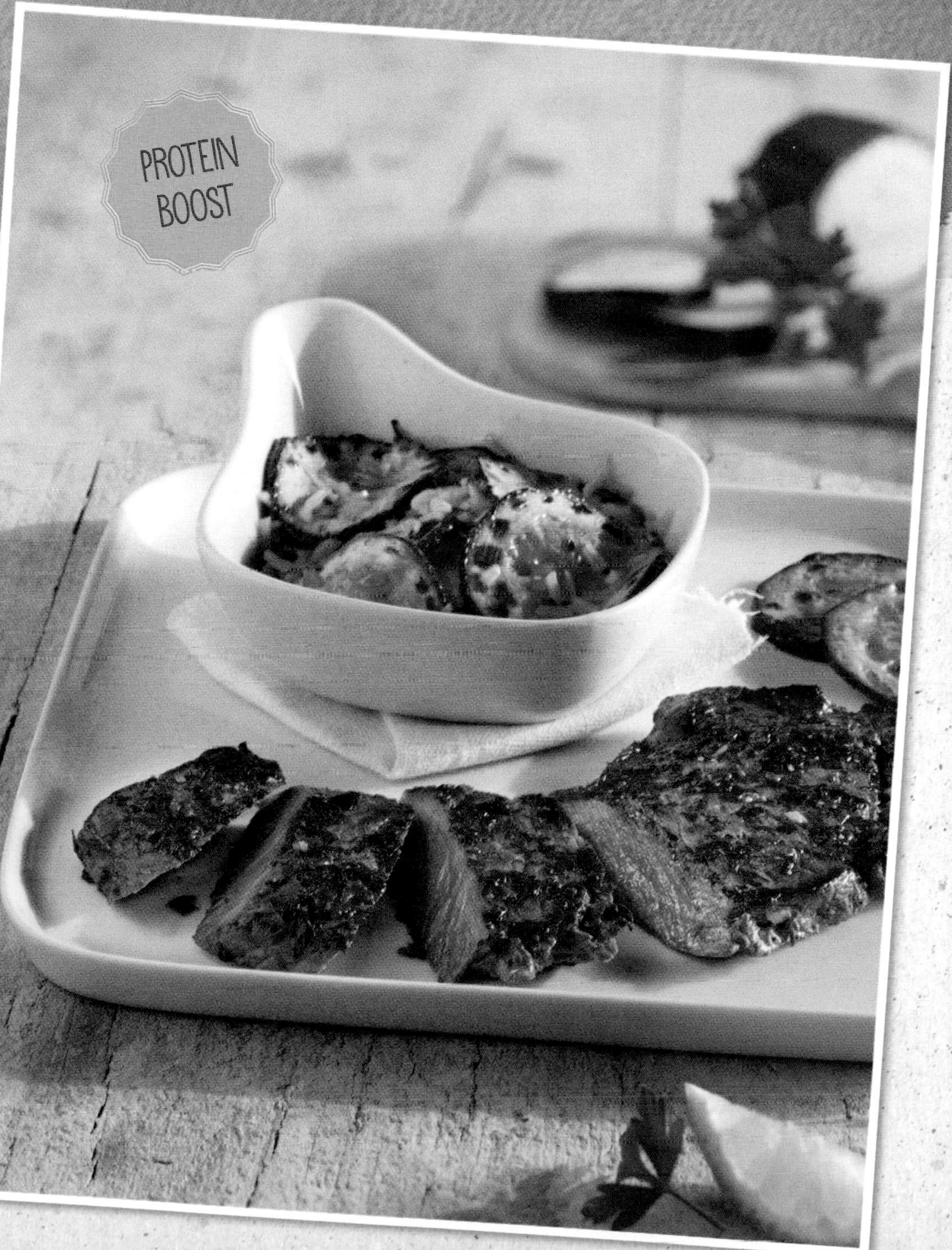
PROTEIN
BOOST

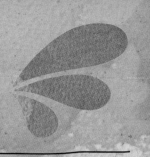

FILLET STEAK
with spicy beans

Serves 4

For the meat:

3 garlic cloves

1 piece root ginger
   (approx. 7 cm)

2 lemongrass stalks

7 tbsp soy sauce

2 tsp raw cane sugar

2 tbsp dry sherry

8 fillet steaks
   (each approx. 90 g)

For the beans:

600 g dwarf beans

salt

1 red chilli

7 shallots

1 garlic clove

1 bunch coriander

pepper

You will also need:

olive oil for frying

■ For the marinade: Peel and finely chop the garlic and ginger. Wash the lemongrass, pat dry, and remove the outer leaves. Cut the stalks in half lengthways and then into pieces approximately 5 cm long. Put it all in a bowl and add the soy sauce, sugar and sherry. Wash the meat, pat it dry, and soak it in the marinade, covered, for about 2 hours. Lift the meat out of the marinade and pat dry. Sieve the marinade and reserve it.

■ Meanwhile wash and trim the beans. Cook in boiling salted water for about 9 minutes until *al dente*. Drain in a sieve. Wash, trim and chop the chilli. Peel and chop the shallots and garlic. Wash the coriander, shake it dry, and pick off the leaves.

■ Heat a large frying pan and add approximately 3 tablespoons of olive oil. Add the meat and brown well on each side for about 2 minutes. Lift the meat out of the pan, wrap in foil, and leave to rest.

■ Fry the shallots briefly in the pan and add the chilli and garlic. Fold in the beans, fry briefly, and season with salt and pepper. Stir in the coriander leaves.

■ Heat the strained marinade in a pot and reduce for about 2 minutes. Add the meat with its juices to the marinade and mix well. Serve the meat with the beans and sauce.

Beef contains lots of high-quality protein with essential amino acids which cannot be produced by the body.

Preparation time:
approx. 40 minutes
(plus marinating time)
Per portion:
approx. 357 kcal/1495 kJ
43 g P, 16 g F, 9 g CH

■ Wash, trim and spin dry the lamb's lettuce, and set it to one side. Make a dressing with the vinegar, mustard, honey, salt, pepper, and 4–5 tablespoons of olive oil, and set it to one side as well.

■ Using a sharp knife, cut off the tips of the chicken wings and separate the wings at the joint. Wash the chicken pieces, pat dry, and season with salt and pepper.

■ Heat the rest of the olive oil in a pan on a medium heat and fry the meat for approximately 30 minutes, stirring a few times. If necessary, turn the temperature down a bit after a while.

■ Peel and finely slice the garlic. Trim the mushrooms, wipe with kitchen paper, and cut them into even slices.

■ Add the garlic and bay leaves to the chicken pieces and fry for another 5 minutes. Wash the tarragon, pat dry, and pick off the leaves. Put them in the pan and de-glaze with the white wine. Reduce the liquid, add the mushrooms, and cook on a low heat for another 4–5 minutes, stirring all the time. De-glaze with a dash of cream and season with salt and pepper. Mix the salad leaves and dressing and serve with the chicken wings.

Serves 4
250 g lamb's lettuce
1 tbsp cider vinegar
2 tsp Dijon mustard
2 tsp honey
salt
pepper
150 ml olive oil
10 chicken wings
8 garlic cloves
400 g mixed mushrooms
2 bay leaves
4 sprigs tarragon
approx. 50 ml white wine
1 dash of cream

Preparation time:
approx. 40 minutes
(plus cooking time)
Per portion:
approx. 714 kcal/2990 kJ
31 g P, 64 g F, 5 g CH

LAMB CURRY
with mixed vegetables

Serves 4

1 tsp coriander seeds

1 tsp black peppercorns

½ tsp cumin seeds

2–3 cloves

2 star anise

1.4 kg lamb shoulder, boneless

salt

3 garlic cloves

1 onion

1 piece root ginger (approx. 2 cm)

2 lemongrass stalks

4 tbsp coconut oil

1 tbsp tomato purée

1 tbsp mild curry powder

500 ml chicken stock

400 ml coconut milk

200 g green beans

200 g carrots

3 spring onions

100 g cherry tomatoes

juice of 1 lime

1 bunch coriander

■ Pre-heat the oven to 180 °C (Gas Mark 4). Using a pestle and mortar, coarsely grind the coriander seeds, peppercorns, cumin seeds, cloves and star anise. Wash the lamb, pat dry, and cut it into 6 roughly equal-size pieces. Rub all over with the spice mix and season with salt. Peel and finely dice the garlic, onion and ginger. Wash the lemongrass and cut it into long sections.

■ Heat the oil in a roasting dish and fry the meat on all sides on a medium heat for 5–7 minutes. Now add the garlic, onion, ginger, lemongrass, tomato purée and curry powder; brown briefly, de-glaze with the stock, and add the coconut milk. Bring to the boil, place on the lowest oven shelf, and simmer uncovered for 45 minutes.

■ Meanwhile wash and trim the beans; blanch in boiling water for 2 minutes. Drain well. Peel the carrots and cut into slices 1 cm thick on the diagonal. Wash and trim the spring onions, and cut the white and pale green parts into thin rings. Wash the tomatoes.

■ Turn the oven temperature down to 160 °C (Gas Mark 3) after 45 minutes. Put the carrots and beans in the roasting dish with the meat, mix them through evenly, and simmer for another 30 minutes. Add the tomatoes for the last 10 minutes of cooking time.

■ Remove the dish from the oven and drizzle the lamb curry with lime juice. Wash the coriander leaves, shake dry, coarsely chop, and sprinkle them over the curry along with the spring onions.

Preparation time:
approx. 40 minutes
(plus cooking time)
Per portion:
approx. 909 kcal/3806 kJ
58 g P, 70 g F, 12 g CH

LIGHT
BUT FILLING

PORK FILLET
with peppers

Serves 4

1 pork fillet (approx. 300 g)

2 sprigs rosemary

1 bunch fresh thyme

pepper

10 slices bacon

2 tbsp ghee or clarified butter

2 red peppers

2 yellow peppers

4 tbsp coconut oil

salt

Preparation time:
approx. 40 minutes
Per portion:
approx. 626 kcal/2621 kJ
38 g P, 50 g F, 5 g CH

■ Wash the meat and pat it dry. Wash the rosemary and thyme, and shake dry. Remove the stalks and coarsely chop the leaves. Mix half of the leaves with some pepper and coat the meat with them. Fold in the tapered end of the meat to make the joint all the same thickness.

■ Wrap the pork fillet in the bacon slices. Heat the ghee in a pan and brown the fillet on both sides for 2–5 minutes. Cover and gently cook the fillet on a low heat for 15–20 minutes.

■ Meanwhile wash, trim and chop the peppers. Heat the oil in the pan and fry the peppers for 10–15 minutes on a medium heat. Season with salt and pepper. Add the remaining herbs to the pepper mixture. Serve with the sliced pork fillet.

TANDOORI CHICKEN
with carrot salad

Preparation time:
approx. 30 minutes
(plus marinating and cooking time)
Per portion:
approx. 386 kcal/1616 kJ
40 g P, 21 g F, 9 g CH

■ Rinse the chicken breasts and pat them dry. Mix the yoghurt and tandoori paste and rub it well into the chicken. Put the chicken into a dish, pour on all of the yoghurt mixture, cover, and marinate in the fridge for 2 hours.

■ Pre-heat the oven to 200 °C (Gas Mark 6). Line a baking tray with aluminium foil. Lift the chicken breasts out of the dish and brush with the marinade. Place on the foil, season with salt, and bake in the oven for 15 minutes. Turn the oven temperature up to 220 °C (Gas Mark 7) on the grill setting and grill the chicken for another 15–20 minutes.

■ For the carrot spaghetti: Peel the carrots, cut them in half, and cut off the ends. Put them through a spiraliser to make thin spaghetti. Make the dressing by whisking together the orange juice and zest, vinegar, both oils, and some salt. Mix the dressing through the carrot spaghetti and leave it for a few minutes for the flavours to develop.

■ Wash the parsley, pat dry, remove the stalks, and chop the leaves finely. Mix it through the carrot salad and sprinkle with both types of sesame seeds. Serve the tandoori chicken with the carrot salad.

Serves 4
For the chicken breasts:
4 chicken breasts
  (each 150 g, skinless)
250 g natural yoghurt
4 tbsp tandoori masala
  paste
salt

For the salad:
4 large carrots (approx.
  250 g)
juice of 1 orange
grated zest of ½ unwaxed
  orange
4 tbsp cider vinegar
2 tbsp sesame oil
4 tbsp olive oil
salt
½ bunch parsley
2 tbsp white sesame seeds
2 tbsp black sesame seeds

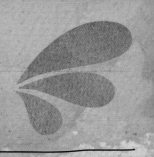

LAMB NOISETTES
with peperonata

Serves 4

For the meat:

700 g lamb noisettes

2 garlic cloves

½ bunch mint

2 sprigs rosemary

½ bunch oregano

10 peppercorns

4 tbsp olive oil

salt

pepper

For the peperonata:

1 small courgette

2 red peppers

2 yellow peppers

1 onion

3 garlic cloves

3 beef tomatoes

1 chilli

3 tbsp small capers

2 tbsp olive oil

salt

pepper

2 tbsp chopped parsley

■ Wash the meat, pat dry, and trim off any excess fat. Peel and slice the garlic. Wash the herbs, shake them dry, and coarsely chop the leaves. Crush the peppercorns in a mortar. Mix all these ingredients with half of the olive oil and rub it into the meat. Wrap in foil and marinate in the fridge for about 4 hours.

■ Pre-heat the oven to 70 °C (under Gas Mark 1, a very cool oven). Warm up an ovenproof dish big enough to accommodate the meat. Scrape the marinade off the lamb. Season with salt and pepper. Heat up the rest of the oil in 2 pans and brown the meat on both sides for about 2 minutes. Put the meat in the ovenproof dish and cook in the oven for another 40 minutes.

■ Meanwhile make the peperonata: Wash, trim and finely dice the courgette. Wash and trim the peppers and cut them into julienne strips. Peel and finely chop the onion and garlic. Remove the tomato stems, make a crosswise incision in the stem ends, cover with boiling water for a few minutes, then remove the skins and seeds. Chop the tomato flesh. Cut the chilli in half, trim, then wash and chop it. Drain and rinse the capers.

■ Heat the olive oil in one of the meat pans. Start by sweating the onion in it, then add the pepper strips, diced courgette, garlic, and chilli. Fry for approximately 5 minutes, stirring all the time, then add the tomatoes. Season with salt and pepper. Simmer uncovered on a low heat for about 10 minutes, and keep stirring. Fold in the parsley before serving the peperonata with the meat.

A MEDITERRANEAN
FAVOURITE

Preparation time:
approx. 50 minutes
(plus marinating and cooking time)
Per portion:
approx. 425 kcal/1779 kJ
40 g P, 23 g F, 14 g CH

POACHED BEEF FILLET
with parsnip purée

Serves 4
For the purée:
1 kg parsnips
salt
200 ml cream
freshly grated nutmeg
pepper
20 g butter

For the meat and sauce:
4 beef fillet steaks
   (each approx. 200 g)
500 ml chicken stock
500 ml red wine
8 garlic cloves
1 bunch thyme
10 peppercorns
80 g butter

Preparation time:
approx. 40 minutes
Per portion:
approx. 681 kcal/2851 kJ
48 g P, 45 g F, 13 g CH

■ For the purée: Wash, trim and dice the parsnips. Cook in a large pan of boiling salted water for about 20 minutes until soft. Drain in a sieve.

■ Wash the steaks and pat them dry. In a pot large enough to hold the fillet steaks next to each other, add the chicken stock, red wine and unpeeled garlic cloves. Wash the thyme and add it to the pot along with the peppercorns. Bring it all to the boil. Turn down the heat, place the steaks in the broth, and poach gently for approximately 7 minutes. Lift them out and wrap them in foil. Reserve the broth.

■ To make the purée, bring the cream to the boil. Add the diced parsnip and some grated nutmeg. Whizz it all until smooth and creamy, season with salt and pepper, and stir in the butter.

■ For the sauce: Measure out 150 ml of the red wine broth, fast boil it in a pan for 5 minutes, and stir in the butter. Serve the steaks with the purée and red wine sauce. Goes well with fried asparagus.

PARSNIPS ARE RICH IN FIBRE, VITAMINS AND MINERALS, ESPECIALLY POTASSIUM.

PORK OLIVES
with ratatouille

Serves 4

For the ratatouille:

2 yellow peppers

2 red peppers

2 small courgettes

2 red onions

3 garlic cloves

250 g cherry tomatoes

1 bunch thyme

3 tbsp olive oil

salt

pepper

250 ml vegetable stock

3 tbsp tomato purée

For the pork olives:

2 bunches basil

30 g Parmesan

30 g pine nuts

5 tbsp olive oil

salt

pepper

75 g sundried tomatoes
  in oil

8 small pork escalopes
(each approx. 75 g)

■ For the ratatouille: Wash and trim the peppers, then cut them into strips. Wash, trim and finely dice the courgettes. Peel the onions and garlic and slice them finely. Wash, trim and halve the tomatoes. Wash the thyme, pat dry, and pick off the leaves.

■ Pre-heat the oven to 180 °C (Gas Mark 4). In a bowl, mix together the peppers, courgettes, onions, garlic and thyme. Add the olive oil, salt and pepper, and combine well. Spread them over a roasting pan and bake in the oven for about 20 minutes.

■ For the pork olives: Wash the basil, shake it dry, and chop the leaves. Grate the Parmesan. Dry-roast the pine nuts in a pan until golden. Whizz half of the basil with the Parmesan, pine nuts, and 3 tablespoons of olive oil until smooth. Season the pesto with salt and pepper.

This tasty dish is also ideal if you have guests to dinner! Served with crispy baguettes, it will be a sure-fire hit – and they will be eating the low-carb way.

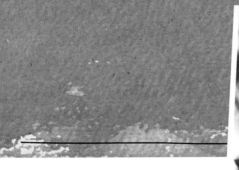

■ Pat the sundried tomatoes dry and cut them into strips. Wash the escalopes, pat dry, and beat them flat with a meat hammer. Season with salt and pepper, and brush them with half of the pesto. Arrange the sundried tomatoes and the rest of the chopped basil on top. Roll the meat up tightly and hold it in place with kitchen string. Heat the remaining oil in a pan and brown the pork olives all over for about 5 minutes.

■ Mix together the vegetable stock and tomato purée and pour it over the oven vegetables after the 20-minute cooking time is up, and add the cherry tomatoes. Place the meat rolls in the mixture and simmer for another 15 minutes. Remove the tray from the oven and serve the dish drizzled with the remaining pesto.

Preparation time:
approx. 1 hour
(plus cooking time)
Per portion:
approx. 489 kcal/2047 kJ
44 g P, 31 g F, 7 g CH

VEAL ROULADES
with ham and egg stuffing

Serves 4

4 eggs

4 veal escalopes

salt

pepper

4 slices beef ham (very thin minute steak)

3 tbsp clarified butter

250 ml veal or beef stock

1 tbsp plain flour

2 tbsp freshly chopped parsley

Preparation time:
approx. 40 minutes
(plus cooking time)
Per portion:
approx. 300 kcal/1256 kJ
36 g P, 15 g F, 3 g CH

■ Hard-boil the eggs and rinse them under cold water. Once they have cooled down, peel them. Wash the veal escalopes, pat dry, and beat them flat. Season with salt and pepper and place a slice of beef ham on top of each.

■ Put a boiled egg on each escalope and roll it up. Tie them in place with kitchen string. Heat the clarified butter in a pan and brown the veal rolls well on all sides. Cover and simmer for 10–15 minutes. Transfer them to a plate and keep them warm. De-glaze the meat juices with the stock and bring to the boil.

■ Mix the flour with a little water and whisk it into the sauce until smooth and velvety. Add the parsley. Serve the roulades with the sauce.

GOES WELL WITH
FRESH GREEN SALAD

PAN-FRIED BOLOGNA
with mushrooms

Preparation time:
approx. 30 minutes
(plus cooking time)
Per portion:
approx. 480 kcal/2010 kJ
19 g P, 43 g F, 7 g CH

■ Remove the sausage skin and slice the meat. Trim and wipe the mushrooms, then cut them into thin slices. Peel and chop the onions and garlic; trim and wash the leek, and cut it into rings.

■ Heat the olive oil in a pan and brown the sausage slices. Add the onions, garlic and leek and simmer for 5 minutes. Mix in the tinned tomatoes and tomato purée and add the meat stock. Stir in the seasoning and herbs and simmer for about 15 minutes on a low heat. Fold in the mushrooms and simmer for another 10 minutes.

■ Adjust the seasoning if required and finish off with the cream. Goes well with fresh leaf salad.

Serves 4

1 bologna (Lyon sausage) ring

150 g button mushrooms

2 onions

1 garlic clove

1 leek

2 tbsp olive oil

400 g peeled tomatoes (tinned)

5 tbsp tomato purée

125 ml meat stock

salt

pepper

dried basil

dried marjoram

paprika powder

2 tbsp cream

ALSO TASTES GREAT MADE
WITH MEAT LOAF!

VEAL CUTLETS
with rocket salad

Serves 4
For the salad:
100 g walnuts
1 tbsp maple syrup
sea salt
200 g rocket

For the meat:
4 veal cutlets
   (each approx. 225 g)
salt
pepper
4 tbsp olive oil

For the dressing:
2 tbsp capers
75 ml lemon juice
75 ml olive oil
salt
pepper

Preparation time:
approx. 25 minutes
Per portion:
approx. 673 kcal/2818 kJ
45 g P, 50 g F, 12 g CH

■   For the salad: Dry-roast the walnuts in a pan, drizzle the maple syrup over them, and caramelise briefly. Sprinkle on some sea salt, transfer to a plate, leave to cool, then chop the walnuts coarsely. Trim, wash, shake dry, then tear the rocket into bite-size pieces.

■   Pre-heat the oven to 120 °C (Gas Mark ½). Line a baking tray with greaseproof paper. Heat 2 frying pans. Wash the cutlets, pat dry, season with salt and pepper, and brown in the hot olive oil for about 2 minutes on each side. Transfer them to the baking tray and cook in the oven for about 9 minutes. Take them out, wrap in foil, and rest the meat for approximately 5 minutes.

■   For the dressing: Rinse the capers and drain well. Combine the lemon juice and olive oil. Add the capers and season with salt and pepper. Arrange the rocket on plates. Sprinkle the caramelised walnuts on top. Place a cutlet on each plate and drizzle with the dressing.

MINUTE STEAKS
with tomato concasse

Serves 4

For the tomatoes:

1 kg cherry tomatoes

2 tsp icing sugar

2 tsp sea salt

2 dried chillies

2 bunches thyme

6 garlic cloves

6 tbsp olive oil

pepper

balsamic vinegar

For the meat:

3 tbsp clarified butter

4 tbsp olive oil

600 g thinly sliced beef
   steaks

salt

pepper

You will also need:

1 bunch sage

■ Pre-heat the fan oven to 150 °C (Gas Mark 2). Line 2 baking trays with greaseproof paper. Wash the tomatoes, pat dry, and remove the stem ends. Cut the tomatoes in half and spread them out over the trays. Dust with the icing sugar, and sprinkle on the salt and crumbled chillies.

■ Wash the thyme, and pat it dry. Place the sprigs on top of the tomatoes. Crush 4 unpeeled garlic cloves and arrange them over the tomatoes as well. Drizzle all over with olive oil and cook in the cool oven for about 40 minutes. When cooked, remove the garlic and thyme; put the tomatoes in a pre-heated bowl and season to taste with salt, pepper, and a dash of balsamic vinegar.

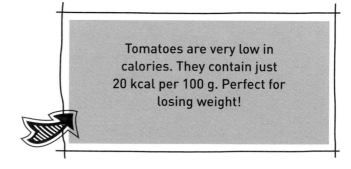

Tomatoes are very low in calories. They contain just 20 kcal per 100 g. Perfect for losing weight!

FAVOURITE DISH

■ Wash the sage, pat dry, and pick off the leaves. Heat 2 frying pans and melt the clarified butter and olive oil in them. Wash the steaks, pat dry, season with salt and pepper, and sear on each side for about 1 minute. Remove from the hob; wrap the steaks immediately in foil and leave to rest for approximately 2 minutes. Fry the sage leaves in the browning juices until crispy. Arrange the steaks and tomatoes on plates and serve sprinkled with the crispy sage and low-carb bread (optional).

Preparation time:
approx. 30 minutes
(plus cooking time)
Per portion:
approx. 487 kcal/2039 kJ
37 g P, 32 g F, 13 g CH

FISH

Omega 3 power

LEMON

CAPERS

DILL

SALMON

PRAWNS

ZANDER FILLET
with bean salad

Serves 4

300 g preserved artichokes (drained weight)

1½ tsp pickled capers

juice and zest of ½ unwaxed lemon

salt

pepper

70 ml olive oil

5 tsp freshly chopped mixed herbs (parsley, chives, basil, tarragon)

300 g fine green beans

4 zander fillets (or other firm-flesh white fish steaks) (each approx. 150 g)

Preparation time:
approx. 25 minutes
(plus cooking time)
Per portion:
approx. 319 kcal/1338 kJ
33 g P, 19 g F, 4 g CH

■ Pre-heat the oven to 180 °C (Gas Mark 4). Drain the artichokes and then the capers in a sieve. Cut the artichokes into bite-size pieces. Finely chop the capers, mix in the lemon juice and zest, season with salt and pepper, and gradually mix in 50 ml of olive oil. Stir in the chopped herbs.

■ Wash and trim the beans; cook in a pan of boiling salted water for 10–12 minutes. Leave to cool down a bit, then cut them in half or into 3. Combine the beans and artichokes with the herb dressing.

■ Wash the fish, pat dry, and rub the remaining olive oil into it. Fry briefly on both sides in a pan (not too hot), season with salt and pepper, then bake in an ovenproof dish for 5–8 minutes.

■ Arrange the artichoke and bean salad on plates and place the fish on top. Serve immediately.

CRISPY SALMON
with walnut salsa verde

Serves 4

For the salsa verde:
100 g walnuts
1 bunch parsley
6 sprigs chives
3 sprigs oregano
6 sprigs thyme
1 spring onion
2 tsp capers
1 garlic clove
90 ml olive oil
pepper
herb salt

For the vegetables and fish:
2 fennel bulbs
1 red onion
3 carrots
4 tbsp oil
4 wild salmon fillets, skin removed (each approx. 250 g)
1 tbsp lime or lemon juice
sea salt
freshly ground pepper

■ Pre-heat the oven to 170 °C (Gas Mark 3). Put the walnut halves on a baking tray lined with greaseproof paper and roast in the oven for about 7 minutes. Leave to cook and chop them coarsely.

■ Meanwhile wash the herbs, pat dry, pick off the leaves and chop them finely. Wash and chop the spring onion. Chop the capers; peel and chop the garlic. Put the parsley, chives, oregano and half of the thyme in a bowl and mix in the garlic and olive oil. Season with pepper and herb salt. Add the capers, spring onion and toasted walnuts to the salsa verde and mix well.

■ Wash, trim and finely slice the fennel. Peel the onion and carrots; finely chop the onion and cut the carrots into slices on the diagonal. Heat 3 tablespoons of oil in a pan and brown the onion; add the carrots and fennel and sweat on a medium heat for 10 minutes, stirring occasionally. Season with salt and pepper and stir in the rest of the thyme.

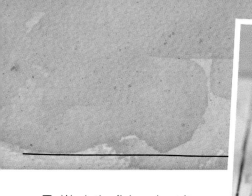

■ Wash the fish and pat it dry. Heat the remaining oil in a large non-stick pan. Fry the salmon fillets for approximately 3 minutes on each side until golden and crispy. Add the lime or lemon juice to the salsa verde and mix well. Arrange the fennel mixture on the plates. Place a salmon fillet on top of each, season with salt and pepper, and serve with the salsa verde.

Preparation time:
approx. 45 minutes
Per portion:
approx. 970 kcal/4061 kJ
56 g P, 79 g F, 12 g CH

COD STEAKS
with shiitake mushrooms

Serves 4

4 cod steaks
   (each approx. 170 g)

salt

juice of ½ lemon

100 g streaky bacon

100 g fresh shiitake
   mushrooms

50 g sundried tomatoes
   in oil

2 tbsp pitted black olives

2 shallots

30 g butter

1 tbsp capers

pepper

Preparation time:
approx. 30 minutes
Per portion:
approx. 328 kcal/1373 kJ
35 g P, 19 g F, 4 g CH

■ Wash the fish and pat it dry. Season with salt and drizzle the lemon juice over it. Finely dice the bacon. Wipe the mushrooms clean with a damp cloth and trim the ends. Cut these and the sundried tomatoes into thin strips. Slice the olives thinly; peel and finely dice the shallots.

■ Heat the butter in a pan and fry the fish on each side for about 4 minutes on a medium heat, turning carefully. Transfer it to a plate and keep it warm.

■ Render the bacon in the hot frying fat. Add the diced shallots and mushrooms and sweat them with the bacon. Add the prepared tomatoes, olives and capers and season with pepper. Serve the fish with the bacon sauce.

Shiitake mushrooms have firm, aromatic flesh. They can easily be dried and then used as seasoning.

SHRIMP CAKES
with remoulade

Preparation time:
approx. 25 minutes
Per portion:
approx. 487 kcal/2039 kJ
38 g P, 36 g F, 2 g CH

■ Finely chop the shrimps (or use a food mixer). Peel and finely chop the onion. Combine all the shrimp cake ingredients and season with salt and pepper.

■ Heat the clarified butter in a pan on a medium heat and fry the cakes on each side for 6–8 minutes until golden brown.

■ Meanwhile make the remoulade: Whizz the egg, mustard and lemon juice with a hand blender or in a food mixer, then add salt and pepper. Drizzle in the oil slowly until you have the desired consistency.

■ Peel the onion and dice it very finely. Drain and finely chop the gherkins and capers. Stir the onion, gherkins, capers and chopped herbs into the egg mixture. Serve the shrimp cakes with the remoulade.

Serves 4
For the shrimp cakes:
500 g North Sea brown
    shrimps, peeled

1 small onion

200 g mixed minced meat
    (beef and pork)

2 eggs

salt

pepper

clarified butter for frying

For the remoulade:
1 egg

1 tsp mustard

1 tbsp freshly squeezed
    lemon juice

salt

pepper

200 ml olive oil

½ onion

3 pickled gherkins

½ tbsp pickled capers

some chopped parsley and
    dill

MARINATED SEA TROUT
with honey and dill sauce

Serves 8
For the marinade:
1 unwaxed lemon
2 bunches dill
1 bunch flat-leaf parsley
2 tbsp coarse sea salt
½ tsp coarsely ground
    pepper
1 large prepared sea
    trout (approx. 1.5 kg,
    left whole with skin on,
    but de-boned)

For the sauce:
1 bunch dill
2 tbsp runny honey
1–2 tbsp horseradish (jar)
1 carton crème fraîche
    (150 g)
salt, pepper

Preparation time:
approx. 30 minutes
(plus chilling time)
Per portion:
approx. 348 kcal/1457 kJ
35 g P, 22 g F, 3 g CH

■ For the marinade: Wash the lemon in hot water, pat dry, and finely grate the zest. Wash the herbs, shake them dry, and finely chop them. Mix these ingredients together with some salt and pepper.

■ Rinse the fish well outside and inside, pat dry, and open it out. Spread the marinade over the inside cavity, then fold the sides of the fish together so that the seasoned sides meet.

■ Wrap the fish in cling film and place it on a platter. Place a chopping board on top of the fish and weigh it down (e.g. with some tins). Leave to marinate in the fridge for three days. Then separate the two halves of the trout and cut them on the diagonal into wafer-thin slices.

■ For the sauce: Chop the dill finely and combine with the honey, horseradish and crème fraîche. Season with salt and pepper and serve with the sea trout.

OMEGA 3
POWER

SEA BREAM
oven-baked

Serves 4

4 prepared sea bream
(each approx. 300 g)

salt

pepper

8 tomatoes

8 garlic cloves

1 bunch coriander

1 bunch dill

6 tbsp olive oil

juice of 2 lemons

harissa paste to taste

2 tsp ground cumin

2 tsp sweet paprika

oil for the baking tray

■ Pre-heat the oven to 175 °C (Gas Mark 3–4). Wash the fish and pat dry. Rub salt and pepper into the cavities. Make three incisions in the skin sides of each fish. Slice the tomatoes and place them overlapping on a greased baking tray.

■ Peel the garlic. Wash the herbs, shake them dry, and whizz them into a paste in a food mixer together with the garlic, olive oil, lemon juice, harissa and spices.

■ Rub some of the herb paste into the incisions in the fish. Place the fish on top of the tomatoes and drizzle the remaining paste over them. Put the tray in the oven for 30 minutes until the fish comes away easily from the bones.

Preparation time:
approx. 1 hour
Per portion:
approx. 477 kcal/1997 kJ
62 g P, 22 g F, 7 g CH

SALMON FILLET
with basil and avocado crust

PROTEIN
BOOST

Preparation time:
approx. 10 minutes
(plus cooking time)
Per portion:
approx. 544 kcal/2278 kJ
42 g P, 40 g F, 5 g CH

■ Grease a baking tray with coconut oil. Pre-heat the oven to 180 °C (Gas Mark 4). Cut the avocado in half, remove the stone, scoop out the flesh and mash with a fork until smooth and creamy. Drain and finely chop the capers; crush the garlic in a garlic press. Chop the basil leaves. Mix the capers, garlic, basil and grated lemon zest through the mashed avocado.

■ Wash the salmon fillets, pat dry, and place them on the baking tray. Spread the avocado paste over them using a knife or the back of a spoon.

■ Bake in the oven for about 10 minutes, then lightly brown the avocado topping under the grill for another 3–4 minutes.

Serves 4

1 avocado
1 tsp pickled capers
3 garlic cloves
1 handful basil leaves
1 tbsp grated zest of an unwaxed lemon
4 wild salmon fillets (each approx. 200 g)
coconut oil for the baking tray

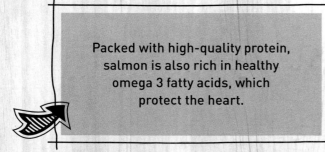

Packed with high-quality protein, salmon is also rich in healthy omega 3 fatty acids, which protect the heart.

SCAMPI
with courgette pasta

Serves 4

4 tbsp pine nuts

8 courgettes

3 garlic cloves

½ unwaxed lemon

150 g cherry tomatoes

5 tbsp olive oil

200 g prepared scampi

salt

pepper

Preparation time:
approx. 30 minutes
(plus cooking time)

Per portion:
approx. 270 kcal/1130 kJ
18 g P, 18 g F, 10 g CH

■ Dry-roast the pine nuts in a pan until they exude a delicious aroma. Take them out of the pan and set to one side.

■ Wash and trim the courgettes, then make them into spaghetti using a spiraliser. Alternatively, you can cut them into long thin slices with a potato peeler and then into julienne strips with a knife. Peel and finely slice the garlic. Rinse the lemon in hot water, grate the zest, and squeeze out the juice. Wash the tomatoes and cut them in half.

■ Put the oil in a deep non-stick frying pan and sweat the garlic; add the scampi and fry them briefly. Add the courgette pasta and fry for 3–5 minutes. Stir in the lemon juice and zest and the tomatoes. Season with salt and pepper, and serve sprinkled with pine nuts.

SUPER
HEALTHY

OMELETTE
with smoked trout

Serves 4

8 spring onions

400 g smoked trout

1 unwaxed lemon

8 eggs

100 ml milk

salt

pepper

80 g Parmesan

4 tbsp butter

1 bunch chives

You will also need:

Parmesan for sprinkling
on top

Preparation time:
approx. 25 minutes
Per portion:
approx. 450 kcal/1884 kJ
44 g P, 27 g F, 7 g CH

■ Wash and trim the spring onions, and pat dry. Cut the white and pale green parts into thin rings. Remove any bones from the fish and break it into bite-size pieces. Rinse the lemon in hot water, pat dry, and grate the zest.

■ Put the eggs and milk in a bowl. Add half a teaspoon of salt and some pepper. Add the finely grated Parmesan. Whisk it all lightly with a fork.

■ Melt the butter in two pans on a medium heat. Divide the spring onions and fish between the pans. Gently sweat for about 5 minutes, stirring well, until both mixtures are well coated in butter. Now pour in the egg mix.

■ Cook on a medium heat for approximately 7 minutes until the surface has set. Meanwhile wash the chives, pat dry and chop them. Cut the omelettes in half immediately and transfer them to plates. Grate some Parmesan on top and sprinkle with chives. Serve with fresh salad if you like.

PARMESAN CONTAINS 36 G OF PROTEIN PER 100 G – HIGHER THAN ANY OTHER TYPE OF CHEESE!

LEMONY SALMON
with baked asparagus

Serves 4
For the salmon:
600 g wild salmon fillet
salt
pepper
1 unwaxed lemon
2 tbsp olive oil

For the asparagus:
500 g white asparagus
500 g green asparagus
1 garlic clove
salt
pepper
5 tbsp olive oil

Preparation time:
approx. 25 minutes
(plus cooking time)
Per portion:
approx. 480 kcal/2010 kJ
35 g P, 35 g F, 6 g CH

■ Pre-heat the oven to 180 °C (Gas Mark 4). Line a baking tray with greaseproof paper. Peel the white asparagus from the tips down, and the bottom third of the green asparagus. Peel and slice the garlic.

■ Arrange the asparagus and garlic on the baking tray. Season with salt and pepper, and drizzle with olive oil. Bake in the oven for about 20 minutes.

■ Wash the salmon fillet, pat dry, and cut it into 4 equal portions. Season with salt and pepper. Rinse the lemon under hot water and slice it.

■ Heat the olive oil in a pan and fry the lemon slices briefly on both sides. Take the lemon slices out of the pan. Fry the salmon on each side for 2–3 minutes; it should still be transparent in the middle. Serve the salmon with the lemon slices and asparagus.

VEGETABLES

fill up on vegetables

SPINACH

SPRING
ONIONS

MUSHROOMS

TOMATOES

TOMATO OMELETTE
with olives

Preparation time:
approx. 10 minutes
(plus cooking time)
Per portion:
approx. 341 kcal/1428 kJ
14 g P, 30 g F, 4 g CH

■ Wash, trim and halve the tomatoes. Wash the thyme, shake it dry, pick off the leaves and chop them finely. Slice the olives.

■ Whisk the eggs and thyme, and season with salt and pepper. Mix in the olives. Heat 1 tablespoon of clarified butter in a pan for each omelette. Add a quarter of the egg mix at a time, topping with a quarter of the tomatoes; cook for about 10 minutes on a medium heat until set. Cook the four omelettes one after the other.

Serves 4

400 g cherry tomatoes
½ bunch thyme
100 g pitted green olives
8 eggs
salt
pepper
4 tbsp clarified butter

EGGS CONTAIN LOTS OF VALUABLE ESSENTIAL SUBSTANCES AND HIGH-QUALITY PROTEIN.

PORTOBELLO MUSHROOMS
deliciously stuffed

Serves 4

1 red pepper

4 large Portobello mushrooms (each approx. 110 g)

1 large Spanish onion

2 medium-size courgettes

6 sundried tomatoes in oil

3 garlic cloves

2 tbsp olive oil

½ tsp dried oregano

chilli flakes

salt

pepper

30 g breadcrumbs

35 g grated Parmesan

1 buffalo mozzarella

Preparation time:
approx. 30 minutes
(plus cooking time)
Per portion:
approx. 255 kcal/1063 kJ
16 g P, 15 g F, 13 g CH

■ Pre-heat the oven to 200 °C (Gas Mark 6). Wash the peppers, pat dry, and place them on a baking tray lined with greaseproof paper. Bake in the oven until the skins turn black, turning several times. Take them out of the oven, but leave it on. Wrap the peppers for a few minutes in a damp kitchen cloth, then carefully remove the blackened skins. Cut the peppers in half, remove the seeds, and finely dice the flesh.

■ Break off the mushroom stems and wipe the mushrooms clean with damp kitchen paper. Peel and finely dice the onion; wash, dry, trim and finely dice the courgettes. Chop the tomatoes. Peel and chop the garlic. Place the mushrooms on a baking tray lined with greaseproof paper and brush with some olive oil. Heat the remaining oil in a pan and sweat the onions. Add the courgettes and sweat for approximately 4 minutes. Add the peppers, sundried tomatoes and garlic and sweat all of these too.

■ Transfer the vegetables to a bowl and season with oregano, chilli flakes and some salt and pepper; stir in the breadcrumbs and Parmesan. Divide the mixture between the 4 mushrooms. Bake in the oven for about 35 minutes. Dice the mozzarella. Divide it between the mushrooms and bake for about 10 minutes until melted.

ROCKET FRITTATA
with goat's cheese

Serves 4

250 g rocket

1 large onion

2 tbsp olive oil

8 eggs

salt

pepper

150 g soft goat's cheese

Preparation time:
approx. 15 minutes
(plus cooking time)

Per portion:
approx. 370 kcal/1549 kJ
20 g P, 31 g F, 5 g CH

■ Wash the rocket, shake it dry, and chop finely, removing any coarse stalks. Peel and finely chop the onion.

■ Heat the olive oil in a large non-stick pan and sweat the onion until it is transparent. Add the rocket and stir-fry for 2–3 minutes. Remove the pan from the hob and leave it to cool down a bit. Pre-heat the oven to 200 °C (Gas Mark 6).

■ Whisk the eggs in a bowl until light and fluffy, and season with salt and pepper. Pour the egg mix into the pan with the fried rocket, distributing it evenly. Arrange dollops of goat's cheese on top and bake the frittata in the oven for 15–18 minutes until set.

AUBERGINE PURÉE
with cucumber salad

Serves 4

1 large cucumber

12 walnut halves

4 tbsp freshly chopped mint

2 tsp lemon juice

½ tsp honey

salt

pepper

135 ml olive oil

6 small aubergines
(each approx. 100 g)

8 garlic cloves

½ tsp turmeric

¼ tsp ground coriander

4 eggs

pink peppercorns (optional)

Preparation time:
approx. 45 minutes
(plus cooking time)
Per portion:
approx. 473 kcal/1983 kJ
11 g P, 44 g F, 10 g CH

■ Wash and peel the cucumber, cut it in half, and scoop out the seeds. If too big, cut the cucumber halves in half again and slice the flesh thinly. Coarsely chop the walnuts and dry-roast them in a pan. Combine them with the cucumber and mint.

■ Make a dressing by mixing together the lemon juice, honey, salt, pepper and 4–5 tablespoons of olive oil; use it to marinate the cucumber mixture.

■ Pre-heat the oven to 200 °C (Gas Mark 6). Wash the aubergines, wipe them dry, and prick them in a few places with a fork so they do not burst when cooking. Place them on a baking tray lined with greaseproof paper; put them under the oven grill until the skin blackens and begins to peel off in places. Keep turning the aubergines over as they brown. Take them out of the oven and leave until cool to the touch. Peel off the burnt skin and coarsely chop the flesh.

■ Peel and finely chop the garlic. Heat 2 tablespoons of olive oil in a non-stick pan and sweat half of the garlic. Sprinkle on the turmeric and coriander, then add the chopped aubergine and stir well. Fry it until all the liquid has evaporated and the mixture is nice and thick.

■ Whisk the eggs in a bowl, and season well with salt. Push the aubergine mix in the pan around the sides to make a well the size of your palm in the middle. Add the remaining olive oil and fry the rest of the garlic until golden. Add the whisked eggs and fry for 2 minutes, then mix it through the aubergines. Cook for another few minutes and serve immediately with the cucumber salad. Garnish with crushed pink peppercorns (optional).

ASPARAGUS
with herb vinaigrette

Preparation time:
approx. 40 minutes
Per portion:
approx. 210 kcal/879 kJ
12 g P, 14 g F, 10 g CH

■ Put the eggs in boiling water and cook for about 8 minutes. Rinse briefly with cold water, leave to cool, and peel them.

■ Peel the asparagus, and snap off the woody ends. Cook the asparagus in boiling salted water with some sugar and the lemon slices for about 8 minutes until *al dente*. Reserve 5 tablespoons of the cooking liquid. Drain the asparagus in a sieve.

■ Finely chop the boiled eggs. Peel and finely dice the onion. Heat 1 tablespoon of olive oil in a pan and sweat the onion. Arrange the asparagus in a shallow serving dish.

■ Make the vinaigrette with the reserved asparagus liquid, lemon juice, the rest of the olive oil and the herbs. Season to taste with a pinch of sugar, salt and pepper; add the diced onion. Pour the onion and herb vinaigrette over the asparagus. Sprinkle with the chopped eggs and serve.

Serves 4

2 eggs

1½ kg asparagus

2 slices unwaxed lemon

1 medium-size red onion

4 tbsp olive oil

2 tbsp freshly squeezed
  lemon juice

2 tbsp flat-leaf parsley,
  finely chopped

2 tbsp finely chopped
  chives

2 tbsp finely chopped
  chervil

sugar

salt

pepper

A LIGHT AND TASTY DISH.
FOR SPRING

FRITTATA
with mushroom medley

Serves 4

400 g mixed mushrooms
  (e.g. button, oyster,
  shiitake)

1 onion

2 garlic cloves

½ bunch fresh oregano

1 tbsp pine nuts

4 tbsp clarified butter

1 tbsp lemon juice

8 eggs

salt

pepper

1 tsp very hot paprika

Preparation time:
approx. 10 minutes
(plus cooking time)
Per portion:
approx. 386 kcal/1616 kJ
16 g P, 33 g F, 5 g CH

■ Wipe the mushrooms thoroughly, but do not wash them; dice them finely. Peel and finely chop the onion and garlic. Wash the oregano, shake it dry, pick off the leaves, and chop them finely.

■ Dry-roast the pine nuts in a pan briefly, then take them out. Heat half of the butter in the pan. Fry the mushrooms, onion and garlic on a high heat for about 5 minutes, then stir in the oregano leaves and lemon juice.

■ Lightly beat the eggs, and season with salt, pepper and paprika. Mix in the mushrooms and pine nuts.

■ Heat up the rest of the clarified butter in the pan. Pour in the egg mixture and cook on a low heat for 15–20 minutes until set. Turn it over carefully and cook for another 5 minutes.

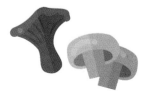

Low in calories and fat, oyster mushrooms contain lots of protein and all the essential amino acids.

SPAGHETTI PIZZA
with squash and pine nuts

Preparation time:
approx. 45 minutes
Per slice:
approx. 104 kcal/434 kJ
5 g P, 7 g F, 4 g CH

■ Pre-heat the oven to 180 °C (Gas Mark 4). Line the spring-form tin with greaseproof paper. Peel the squash and cut off the top end; cut the squash in half, scoop out the seeds, and cut it into thin spaghetti using a spiraliser.

■ Mix the squash spaghetti well with the whisked eggs and chickpea flour. Season with salt and pepper, transfer the mixture to the spring-form, and press down firmly. Bake in the oven for about 20 minutes. Crumble the manouri on top and bake for another 15 minutes.

■ Pick over the rocket, wash it, and shake dry. Dry-roast the pine nuts. Spread the rocket over the squash pizza base and sprinkle with the pine nuts. Cut into wedges and serve immediately.

**Makes 12 slices
(24 cm spring-form tin)**

1 butternut squash (approx. 800 g)

2 eggs

2 tbsp chickpea flour

salt

pepper

200 g manouri (Greek soft cheese)

125 g rocket

3 tbsp pine nuts

Manouri is a creamy Greek soft cheese containing 60–80 % fat. You can replace it with full-fat ricotta.

SOY BEAN TART
with cheddar

**Makes 12 slices
(28 cm tart tin)**

2 onions

2 garlic cloves

2 tbsp butter

650 g cooked soy beans

1 bunch thyme

2 eggs

100 ml milk

100 ml cream

150 g cheddar cheese

salt

pepper

180 g filo pastry

You will also need:

melted butter to grease the
   tin and brush the top of
   the tart

Preparation time:
approx. 20 minutes
(plus cooking time)
Per slice:
approx. 230 kcal/963 kJ
11 g P, 13 g F, 9 g CH

■ Pre-heat the oven to 200 °C (Gas Mark 6). Grease the tart tin with butter. Peel and chop the onions and garlic. Heat the butter and sweat both ingredients, then transfer them to a bowl. Mix in the soy beans. Wash the thyme, pat dry, pick off the leaves and add them to the bean mix.

■ Whisk together the eggs, milk and cream and add to the beans. Grate the cheese and stir half into the mixture. Season with salt and pepper.

■ Line the greased tart tin with the filo sheets, one at a time, brushing each layer with melted butter as you go. Put the filling on top. Sprinkle with the remaining cheese and bake for approximately 30 minutes.

We have long since known that soy beans are very healthy. This tart proves that they also taste great!

QUINOA RISOTTO
with mushrooms

Serves 4

1 garlic clove

30 g hazelnuts

salt

grated zest of 1 unwaxed lemon

2 shallots

650 g button mushrooms

1 bunch flat-leaf parsley

70 g quinoa

2 tbsp olive oil

pepper

100 g baby spinach

30 g grated Parmesan

20 g butter

pink peppercorns (optional)

Preparation time:
approx. 30 minutes
(plus cooking time)
Per portion:
approx. 267 kcal/1118 kJ
14 g P, 18 g F, 14 g CH

■ Peel the garlic and whizz in a blender until smooth with the hazelnuts, some salt, and the lemon zest. Set to one side.

■ Peel and finely dice the shallots. Trim the mushrooms, wipe with damp kitchen paper, and slice thinly. Wash the parsley, shake it dry, pick off the leaves and chop them finely. Rinse the quinoa well in a sieve under running water and drain.

■ Heat the olive oil in a pan and sweat the shallots until they begin to turn pale golden. Add the mushrooms and brown them, then the quinoa and 500 ml of hot water, and mix well. Season with salt and pepper and simmer for about 15 minutes until the quinoa is soft and all the liquid has been absorbed. If necessary, add some more water; keep stirring frequently.

■ Add the parsley and spinach, then the Parmesan and butter, combining it all well. Adjust the seasoning and serve sprinkled with the hazelnut mix. Garnish with crushed pink peppercorns (optional).

MEAL IN A MUG

EGG SOUFFLÉ
on tomato carpaccio

Makes 2 mugs (each approx. 360 ml)

2 full-flavoured tomatoes on the vine

salt

pepper

1 tsp balsamic vinegar

1 tbsp olive oil

2 sprigs basil

1 bunch chives

1 tsp butter

4 egg whites

4 tbsp freshly grated pecorino cheese

■ Wash the tomatoes, pat dry, and remove the stem ends. Slice as thinly as possible and spread them over 2 dessert plates. Season with salt and pepper. Drizzle a few drops of balsamic vinegar and olive oil over each plate.

■ Wash the basil, pat dry, and cut the leaves into strips. Place them on top of the tomatoes. Wash the chives, pat dry, and chop them. Divide the butter between the two mugs. Put them in the microwave at 800 watts for 30 seconds each. Brush the melted butter around the inside of the mugs.

■ Put the egg whites in a bowl and stir in some salt, pepper, the chives and cheese, but do not beat them. Divide the mixture between the mugs. Put each mug in the microwave at 600 watts for about 1 minute 10 seconds until the mixture sets. Turn them out onto the tomato carpaccio.

Preparation time:
approx. 15 minutes
Per mug:
approx. 200 kcal/837 kJ
16 g P, 15 g F, 2 g CH

KIDNEY BEAN QUICHE
with chilli cheese

**Makes 6 slices
(22 cm tart tin)**

400 g kidney beans (tinned, drained weight)

5 large eggs

5 egg whites

salt

pepper

100 g cheese with chilli

120 g tomatoes

80 ml water

You will also need:

fat for greasing the tin

coriander for garnish

■ Pre-heat the oven to 200 °C (Gas Mark 6). Grease the tart tin liberally. Put the beans in a sieve, run them under cold water, and drain well.

■ In a large bowl, whisk up the eggs, egg whites, 80 ml water, approximately ½ teaspoon of salt and about ¼ teaspoon of pepper. Pour the egg mix into the tin.

■ Grate the cheese; wash and trim the tomatoes, then cut them into small pieces or thin slices. Arrange the cheese, tomatoes and kidney beans on top of the egg mix.

■ Bake the quiche in the oven for about 30 minutes until the egg has set and is starting to brown. Remove the quiche from the oven, leave to rest for 10 minutes, and serve sprinkled with coriander leaves.

THE CHILLI-FLAVOURED CHEESE GIVES THIS ELEGANT TEX-MEX QUICHE AN ADDED DIMENSION!

Preparation time:
approx. 15 minutes
(plus cooking and resting time)
Per slice:
approx. 218 kcal/912 kJ
20 g P, 10 g F, 12 g CH

STIR-FRY PAK CHOI
with tofu and mushrooms

Serves 4

1 unwaxed lemon

1 piece root ginger (approx. 1 cm)

2 tsp honey

6 tbsp toasted sesame oil

1 tsp salt

400 g plain tofu

4 baby pak choi

500 g small chestnut mushrooms

2 onions

2 garlic cloves

1 pinch chilli powder

3 tbsp sesame seeds

Preparation time:
approx. 30 minutes
(plus cooking time)
Per portion:
approx. 220 kcal/921 kJ
13 g P, 12 g F, 11 g CH

■ Wash the lemon in hot water, grate the zest, and squeeze out the juice. Peel the ginger and chop or grate it very finely. Make a marinade by combining the lemon zest and juice, ginger, honey, 1 tablespoon of oil and salt. Take the tofu out of the packet, drain, and finely dice it. Combine it with the marinade , cover, and leave to soak for about 30 minutes.

■ Wash and trim the pak choi, and cut it into small strips. Trim and wipe the mushrooms, cutting larger ones in half. Peel and finely chop the onions and garlic. Put the mushrooms in a hot pan without fat and brown them, stirring occasionally, until all the excess liquid has evaporated. Scoop the mushrooms out of the pan.

■ Put the rest of the oil in the pan and fry the onions and garlic. Add the tofu and fry on a medium heat, turning occasionally, for about 10 minutes until crispy. Add the pak choi, season with salt, and add the chilli powder; fry all this for another 10 minutes until the pak choi is cooked. Then put the mushrooms back in the pan and heat them up again briefly. Serve sprinkled with sesame seeds.

SNACKS

farewell to hunger pangs!

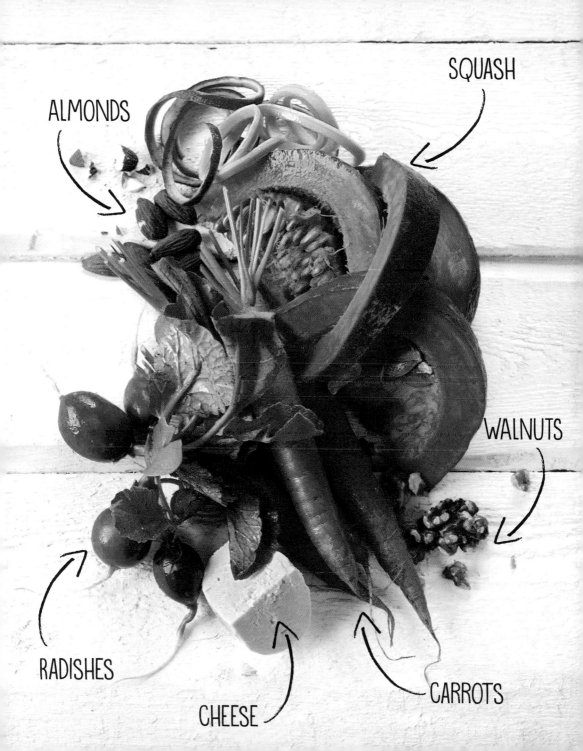

SQUASH

ALMONDS

WALNUTS

RADISHES

CHEESE

CARROTS

BROCCOLI MUFFINS
with pesto

Makes 6
For the pesto:
½ bunch fresh basil
1 small garlic clove
50 g almonds
75 ml olive oil
salt
pepper

For the muffins:
1 onion
1 tbsp coconut oil
100 g broccoli
100 g bacon
4 eggs

Preparation time:
approx. 30 minutes
(plus cooking time)
Per portion:
approx. 170 kcal/712 kJ
9 g P, 14 g F, 1 g CH

■ Wash the basil, and shake it dry. Peel the garlic. Coarsely chop all the ingredients for the pesto, adding 2 tablespoons of water; mash finely with a pestle and mortar or whizz in a blender until smooth.

■ Pre-heat the oven to 180 °C (Gas Mark 4). Peel and finely chop the onion. Heat the coconut oil on a medium heat in a pan and sweat the onions until transparent. Wash and trim the broccoli; chop it and the bacon finely. Add both to the onions and sweat it all until the broccoli is soft.

■ Combine this mixture in a large bowl with the eggs and 2–3 tablespoons of the pesto. You can store any remaining pesto in a sealed container to use for something else.

■ Line a 6-mould muffin tray with greaseproof paper. Divide the mixture between the moulds and bake in the oven for about 30 minutes. Remove the muffins from the moulds. Serve with some pesto.

WITH
BACON

SQUASH WEDGES
oven-baked

Serves 4

1 large hokkaido
  (or red kuri) squash
  (approx. 1 kg)
1 tsp salt
2 dried chillies
½ tsp fennel seeds
1 garlic clove
2 tbsp olive oil

Preparation time:
approx. 20 minutes
(plus cooking time)
Per portion:
approx. 107 kcal/451 kJ
3 g P, 5 g F, 12 g CH

■ Pre-heat the oven to 200 °C (Gas Mark 6) and line a baking tray with greaseproof paper. Wash the squash, cut off the stem end, and cut it in half. Scoop the seeds out with a spoon and cut the squash into wedges.

■ Finely grind the salt, chillies and fennel seeds with a pestle and mortar. Peel the garlic and crush it in the mortar, then add the olive oil to the garlic and spice mix.

■ Brush the squash wedges with the spicy oil and place them on the baking tray. Bake in the oven for 30 minutes until the squash is soft.

# BAKED CHICORY
with ham

Serves 4

4 chicory heads
   (each approx. 200 g)

150 g Emmental cheese

8 sage leaves

40 g butter

3 tbsp orange juice

salt

pepper

8 slices Black Forest ham

Preparation time:
approx. 20 minutes
(plus cooking time)

Per portion:
approx. 313 kcal/1315 kJ
18 g P, 24 g F, 6 g CH

■ Pre-heat the oven to 200 °C (Gas Mark 6). Trim the chicory and cut it in half lengthways. Cut out the hard inner core in a wedge shape. Grate the Emmental. Wash the sage and pat it dry.

■ Heat the sage in the butter and orange juice until foamy. Place the chicory halves cut side down in the butter and cook on a medium heat for about 5 minutes.

■ Take the chicory out of the pan, place one sage leaf on each half, and season lightly with salt and pepper. Wrap a slice of ham round each chicory half, and place them in a baking dish. Sprinkle the cheese on top, then pour the butter from the pan over the chicory. Bake in the oven for approximately 20 minutes until golden brown.

CRISPY KALE
super crunchy

Serves 4
500 g kale
6 tbsp olive oil
1 tsp salt
1 tsp sweet or hot paprika

Preparation time:
approx. 10 minutes
(plus drying time)
Per portion:
approx. 245 kcal/1026 kJ
5 g P, 24 g F, 3 g CH

■ Remove the tough centre stalks of the kale and tear the leaves up roughly. Wash and drain well. Dry the leaves in a salad spinner or shake them in a kitchen cloth.

■ Pre-heat the oven to 130 °C (just under Gas Mark 1). Combine the oil, salt and paprika in a bowl, then add the kale; mix and knead the leaves with your hands, until they are covered all over with the seasoning.

■ Spread the kale leaves on a baking tray lined with greaseproof paper. Make sure there is space between them and that they do not overlap. Dry them in the oven for 30–40 minutes, opening the oven door a few times to release the steam and make the kale nice and crispy. Store in a dry airtight container.

MEATBALLS
with sesame seeds

Makes 20

1 onion

1 garlic clove

500 g mixed minced
    meat (beef and pork)

1 tsp salt

pepper

1 tsp turmeric

1 tbsp harissa paste

1 egg

1–2 tbsp coconut flour as
    required

60 g sesame seeds

coconut oil for frying

Preparation time:
approx. 20 minutes

Per meatball:
approx. 86 kcal/360 kJ
6 g P, 6 g F, 1 g CH

■ Peel the onion and dice it very finely. Peel the garlic and crush it in a garlic press. Combine them both with the mince, salt, pepper, turmeric, harissa and egg, kneading it all well with your hands. If the mixture is too soft, mix in some coconut flour as required.

■ Shape the mixture into about 20 little balls, about 4–5 cm in diameter, and coat them with sesame seeds.

■ Heat the coconut oil in a pan and fry the mince balls all over for about 6 minutes on a medium heat.

BRAISED CARROTS
with herb quark

Serves 4

2 bunches small young
   carrots

2 tbsp oil

500 ml clear vegetable
   stock

1 tbsp honey

juice of 2 oranges

500 g quark (20 % fat)

1 spring onion

1 bunch chives

1 bunch flat-leaf parsley

8 radishes

salt

pepper

■ Trim the carrots, and cut them in half lengthways or leave them whole, depending on the thickness. Heat the oil in a pan and fry the carrots. Put the stock, honey and orange juice in another pan and bring to the boil. Add the carrots, cover, and simmer for about 10 minutes on medium heat.

■ Meanwhile put the quark in a bowl and stir well until smooth and creamy. Wash, trim and finely chop the spring onion and chives. Pick off the parsley leaves and chop them finely. Wash and trim the radishes; dice them very finely. Add the spring onion, herbs and diced radishes to the quark and mix well. Season to taste with salt and pepper.

■ Arrange the carrots on plates with the honey and orange broth and serve with the herb quark.

Preparation time:
approx. 25 minutes
Per portion:
approx. 267 kcal/1118 kJ
20 g P, 8 g F, 8 g CH

COURGETTE PASTA
with bacon

Serves 4

4 slices bacon

1 avocado

1 garlic clove

2 tbsp freshly squeezed
   lime juice

1 tbsp chopped coriander

1 good pinch chilli powder

1 tbsp olive oil

salt

pepper

4 medium-size courgettes

Preparation time:
approx. 20 minutes
(plus cooking time)
Per portion:
approx. 196 kcal/819 kJ
6 g P, 16 g F, 7 g CH

■ Fry the bacon in a non-stick pan without fat until crispy. Drain on kitchen paper and leave to cool, then crumble it.

■ Cut the avocado in half, remove the stone, and scoop out the flesh. Peel the garlic clove. In a tall-sided container, whizz the avocado flesh, garlic, lime juice, coriander, chilli powder and olive oil with a food mixer or hand blender until smooth. Season to taste with salt and pepper.

■ Wash and trim the courgettes; make them into 'pasta' with a spiraliser. Blanch in boiling salted water for about 4 minutes. Strain in a sieve, rinse briefly under cold water, and leave to drain completely. Combine them with the avocado purée, divide between 4 plates, and serve sprinkled with the bacon.

WITH
AVOCADO

PAPRIKA MUFFINS
with ham

Preparation time:
approx. 10 minutes
(plus cooking time)
Per muffin:
approx. 124 kcal/519 kJ
13 g P, 7 g F, 2 g CH

■ Pre-heat the oven to 180 °C (Gas Mark 4). Grease a 6-mould muffin tray. Finely dice the ham; wash the pepper, pat dry, cut in half lengthways, remove the seeds, membranes and stem end, and finely dice the flesh. Peel and finely dice the onions.

■ Whisk the eggs in a large bowl; mix in the ham, pepper, onions, salt and pepper, and 2 tablespoons of water. Divide the mixture between the muffin moulds and bake in the pre-heated oven until the muffins have set in the middle. Take them out of the tray while still warm.

Makes 6
175 g cooked ham
1 red pepper
2 onions
6 eggs
salt
pepper
coconut oil for the
   muffin tray

CARROT NESTS
with tomato medley

Makes 12

1 bunch chives

500 g carrots

150 g cherry tomatoes,
    mixed colours

1 mozzarella ball

3 eggs

100 ml cream

50 g grated Parmesan

salt

pepper

butter to grease the moulds

Preparation time:
approx. 25 minutes
(plus cooking time)
Per nest:
approx. 109 kcal/455 kJ
6 g P, 8 g F, 4 g CH

■ Pre-heat the oven to 180 °C (Gas Mark 4). Grease the moulds of a muffin tray or 12 small individual muffin moulds with butter.

■ Wash the chives, shake them dry, and chop them. Peel and trim the carrots, cut them in half, and make them into thin spaghetti using a spiraliser. Cut the pasta into shorter lengths. Wash, dry, trim and quarter the tomatoes. Break the mozzarella into small pieces.

■ Whisk together the eggs, cream, Parmesan and half of the chives. Season with salt and pepper.

■ Shape the carrot pasta into nests and place them in the muffin moulds. Arrange the tomatoes on top. Pour on the egg mix and top with mozzarella pieces. Bake in the oven for 20–25 minutes until golden brown. Sprinkle with the rest of the chives and serve.

WALNUT AND LEEK CRACKERS
with apricots

Makes 30–50

1 small leek (approx. 130 g)

100 g walnut kernels

50 g sesame seeds

8 dried apricots

1 medium-size courgette (approx. 200 g)

2 tsp salt

50 g mustard or alfalfa sprouts

3 tsp psyllium husks

Preparation time:
approx. 20 minutes
(plus soaking and drying time)
Per cracker:
approx. 33 kcal/138 kJ
1 g P, 2 g F, 2 g CH

■ Thoroughly wash and trim the leek, then cut it into thin rings. Soak it with the walnuts and sesame seeds for 6–8 hours. Soak the apricots for 1–2 hours. Wash, trim and coarsely chop the courgette.

■ Whizz the leek, walnuts, sesame seeds, apricots, courgette and salt in a food mixer until smooth. Mix in the mustard or alfalfa sprouts and psyllium husks, roll the dough out between 2 sheets of greaseproof paper until approximately 5 mm thick. Lift off the top paper and make grooves in the dough with a pastry scraper or the back of a knife to make it easier to break the crackers up later.

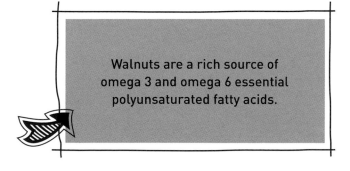

Walnuts are a rich source of omega 3 and omega 6 essential polyunsaturated fatty acids.

■ Arrange the dough with the greaseproof paper on the trays of a food dehydrator, or on a baking tray. If using a dehydrator, set it at 60 °C for the first 30 minutes, then turn it down to 40 °C; or dry it in an oven, leaving the oven door slightly ajar, set at 65 °C, then at 50 °C for 7–9 hours.

■ Remove the greaseproof paper; turn the cracker dough over and leave to dry for another 6–12 hours. Take it out of the oven and break it into individual crackers. Store in a dry airtight container.

AUBERGINE BOATS
with omelette strips

Serves 4

2 large aubergines

5 tbsp olive oil

4 tomatoes

2 mozzarella balls

1 handful basil leaves

50 g Alpine cheese
  (e.g. Gruyère)

6 eggs

salt

pepper

1 tbsp butter

Preparation time:
approx. 45 minutes
(plus cooking time)
Per portion:
approx. 355 kcal/1490 kJ
18 g P, 27 g F, 10 g CH

■ Pre-heat the oven to 200 °C (Gas Mark 6). Line a baking tray with greaseproof paper. Wash the aubergines, pat dry, and cut them in half lengthways. Place them on the baking tray and rub 1 tablespoon of olive oil into the cut surface of each aubergine. Bake in the oven for about 25 minutes until the aubergines are soft.

■ Meanwhile wash the tomatoes, pat dry, and slice them. Slice the mozzarella. Wash the basil and pat it dry.

■ Grate the cheese. Whisk the eggs well, and season with salt and pepper. Heat the remaining olive oil and the butter in a non-stick pan. Pour in the eggs and cook on a medium heat until set.

■ Using a spatula, push the eggs along the bottom of the pan into the middle three times; leave to set again for 2–3 minutes on a low heat. Sprinkle on the cheese and allow it to melt. Fold the omelette over in half and finish cooking for 1–2 minutes.

■ Season the aubergines with salt and pepper. Arrange the sliced tomatoes and then the mozzarella on top and bake in the oven for about 5 minutes until the mozzarella has melted. Arrange the aubergines on plates and sprinkle with basil leaves. Cut the omelette into strips and serve with the aubergines.

STUFFED ONIONS
with kale

Serves 4

30 g clarified butter

1 pack frozen kale (approx. 450 g)

white pepper

ground nutmeg

4 Spanish onions

salt

3 tbsp breadcrumbs

oil or butter for the baking dish

Preparation time:
approx. 20 minutes
(plus cooking time)

Per portion:
approx. 175 kcal/733 kJ
7 g P, 10 g F, 13 g CH

■ Heat about 20 g of the clarified butter in a pot and add the kale, slightly thawed. Cook on a medium heat for about 45 minutes.

■ Season to taste with the spices. Meanwhile peel the onions and cook them in boiling salted water for about 15 minutes.

■ Pre-heat the oven to 220 °C (Gas Mark 7). Lift the onions out of the pot with a skimmer and drain. Leave to cool for a bit, then slice off the tops of the onions and hollow out the middle. Finely chop the tops and the insides, and combine them with the cooked kale.

■ Stuff the onions with the mixture. Grease a baking dish and place the onions in it. Sprinkle with the breadcrumbs and the rest of the flaked clarified butter. Bake in the oven for approximately 15 minutes.

SMOOTHIES

vitamin boosts

SEEDS

PAPAYA

SPINACH

BANANA

BERRIES

BEETROOT SMOOTHIE
with papaya

Serves 2

1 tbsp flaxseeds
4 beetroot leaves
100 g baby spinach
1 grapefruit
1 lemon
1 papaya
1 handful of ice cubes

Preparation time:
approx. 10 minutes
(plus soaking time)
Per portion:
approx. 80 kcal/335 kJ
3 g P, 2 g F, 11 g CH

■ Soak the flaxseeds in cold water for approximately 1 hour. Drain in a sieve. Whizz in a blender with 100 ml of water until smooth.

■ Wash, trim and chop the beetroot and spinach leaves. Put them in the blender. Squeeze the juice from the grapefruit and lemon and pour it into the blender.

■ Peel the papaya, cut it in half, remove the seeds and chop the flesh. Put this in the blender as well, and whizz it all to a smooth purée with 100 ml of water. Add the ice cubes and whizz them until they are completely crushed.

Papaya contains the proteolytic enzyme called papain. It promotes the breakdown of proteins and aids digestion.

WATERCRESS SMOOTHIE
with hazelnuts

Serves 2

30 g hazelnuts

1 pinch chilli powder

100 g watercress

50 g romaine lettuce

4 sprigs basil

½ lemon

½ fennel bulb, with green stalks

1 handful of ice cubes

100 ml sparkling mineral water

freshly ground pepper for garnish

Preparation time:
approx. 15 minutes
(plus soaking time)
Per portion:
approx. 130 kcal/544 kJ
4 g P, 10 g F, 4 g CH

■ Cover the hazelnuts with cold water and soak for about 6 hours. Drain in a sieve and whizz in a blender until smooth with 200 ml of water and the chilli powder.

■ Wash and trim the watercress and lettuce. Wash the basil. Chop it all coarsely and put it in the blender. Squeeze the juice from the lemon and add it too.

■ Wash, trim and chop the fennel, then add it to the blender. Whizz the mixture until it is nice and smooth. Add the ice cubes. Whizz until it is a silky smooth consistency. Finally add about 100 ml of mineral water and whizz briefly. Serve sprinkled with some pepper.

THIS GREEN SMOOTHIE WILL INVIGORATE YOU!

POWER
DRINK

PAPAYA SMOOTHIE
with nuts and seeds

Serves 2

35 g hazelnuts

35 g sunflower seeds

35 g hemp seeds

1 tbsp flaxseeds

3 tbsp dried white
  mulberries

½ papaya

½ lemon

1 handful of ice cubes

Preparation time:
approx. 5 minutes
(plus soaking time)
Per portion:
approx. 310 kcal/1298 kJ
12 g P, 21 g F, 15 g CH

■ Cover the hazelnuts with plenty of cold water and soak for about 6 hours, or overnight. Add the sunflower seeds for the last 2 hours of soaking time.

■ Add the hemp and flaxseeds approximately 1 hour before the end of soaking time. Put the mulberries in another bowl and cover with 300 ml of water. Soak for about 1 hour.

■ Transfer the nuts and seeds to a sieve, rinse, and put in the blender. Add the mulberries with their soaking water and whizz it all until smooth.

■ Peel the papaya, remove the seeds, and chop the flesh. Squeeze the juice from the lemon and put it in the blender with chopped papaya. Whizz the mixture until completely smooth. Add the ice cubes. Whizz until it is a velvety consistency.

PAPAYAS ARE VERY GOOD FOR THE DIGESTION, AS THEY ARE VIRTUALLY FREE FROM FRUIT ACIDS.

HOT!

VEGETABLE SMOOTHIE
with Tabasco

Serves 2

½ cucumber

½ red pepper

½ spring onion

250 ml tomato juice

3 tsp lemon juice

2 tsp Worcestershire sauce

¼ tsp salt

¼ tsp pepper

¼ tsp Tabasco

crushed ice

■ Wash and peel the cucumber; scoop out the seeds with a teaspoon. Wash and trim the pepper and pat dry. Wash and trim the spring onion. Chop them all up.

■ Put all the ingredients except the ice into the blender and whizz until you have the right consistency. Put it in the freezer compartment for at least 30 minutes.

■ Divide the smoothie between 2 glasses, top with crushed ice, and stir once. Serve immediately.

Preparation time:
approx. 10 minutes
(plus freezing time)
Per portion:
approx. 60 kcal/251 kJ
2 g P, 0 g F, 9 g CH

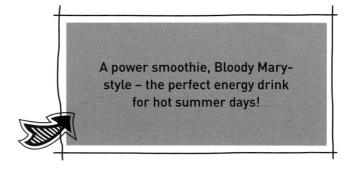

A power smoothie, Bloody Mary-style – the perfect energy drink for hot summer days!

SPINACH SMOOTHIE
with yoghurt

Serves 2

100 g leaf spinach, frozen

10 g sundried tomatoes

100 g natural yoghurt

a few thyme leaves

salt

pepper

some lemon juice

1 pinch sugar

cherry tomatoes and
    thyme sprigs for garnish
    (optional)

Preparation time:
approx. 5 minutes
(plus thawing time)
Per portion:
approx. 100 kcal/419 kJ
7 g P, 4 g F, 6 g CH

■ Thaw the spinach in a blender for about 15 minutes; add the sundried tomatoes, yoghurt and a few thyme leaves (washed and patted dry). Whizz it all until it is a smooth consistency.

■ Season to taste with salt, pepper, lemon juice and a pinch of sugar. Divide between 2 glasses. Garnish with cherry tomatoes and sprigs of thyme (optional).

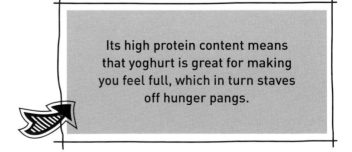

Its high protein content means
that yoghurt is great for making
you feel full, which in turn staves
off hunger pangs.

MOCCACHINO SMOOTHIE
with banana and avocado

Serves 2
1 small banana
½ small avocado
200 ml cold coffee
½ tsp vanilla powder
2 tsp cocoa powder
some crushed ice

Preparation time:
approx. 10 minutes
Per portion:
approx. 150 kcal/628 kJ
4 g P, 9 g F, 13 g CH

■ Peel and chop the banana. Cut the avocado in half, remove the stone and peel, and chop the flesh.

■ Put the banana and avocado in a blender with all the other ingredients and whizz gently.

YOU CAN ALSO WHIZZ A HANDFUL OF PROTEIN-RICH OAT FLAKES INTO THE SMOOTHIE!

DESSERTS

Sweet temptations

RASPBERRIES

EGGS

MINT

VANILLA

ALMONDS

APRICOTS

FROZEN YOGHURT
with peanut butter

Serves 4

1 banana

320 g natural Greek
  yoghurt

60 ml full-fat milk

115 g smooth peanut butter

seeds of ½ vanilla pod

6–8 tbsp erythritol

1 pinch salt

60 ml cream

Preparation time:
approx. 10 minutes
(plus freezing time)
Per portion:
approx. 350 kcal/1465 kJ
11 g P, 26 g F, 18 g CH

■ Peel and chop the banana. Put the yoghurt, milk, peanut butter, chopped banana, vanilla seeds, erythritol and salt into a blender (or use a hand blender) and whizz until smooth. Whip the cream until stiff peaks form and fold it into the purée.

■ Pour the mixture into a shallow container and freeze for 2–3 hours. Every 15 minutes, mix it well with a whisk to prevent ice crystals from forming.

■ When ready to serve, let the frozen yoghurt thaw slightly if necessary, and mix it all well again until creamy. Put the mixture in a piping bag and divide it between dessert glasses.

ALMOND CREAM
with white almond butter

Serves 4

50 g ground almonds
(skin on)

2 egg yolks

80 g erythritol

2½ tbsp cornflour

500 ml full-fat milk

1 tbsp white almond butter

Preparation time:
approx. 25 minutes
(plus cooking time)
Per portion:
approx. 231 kcal/967 kJ
9 g P, 16 g F, 12 g CH

■ Dry-roast the almonds in a pan and set to one side. Beat the egg yolks and erythritol until pale and creamy. In a large bowl, mix the cornflour with 6 tablespoons of the milk until smooth and stir in the egg yolk mixture. Bring the rest of the milk to the boil, immediately turn off the heat, and gradually whisk it into the cornflour mixture.

■ Return the mixture to the pan and bring back to the boil briefly, stirring all the time. Remove from the hob, and stir in three-quarters of the almonds and the almond butter. Pour the cream into dessert bowls and serve sprinkled with the rest of the almonds.

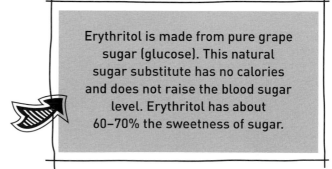

Erythritol is made from pure grape sugar (glucose). This natural sugar substitute has no calories and does not raise the blood sugar level. Erythritol has about 60–70% the sweetness of sugar.

VANILLA CUSTARD
with raspberries

■ Slit the vanilla pod in half lengthways and scrape out the seeds. Put the vanilla seeds and pod in a pan along with the milk and erythritol.

■ Spoon off 5 tablespoons of the milk, and mix it to a smooth paste in a bowl with the egg yolks and cornflour.

■ Heat the milk mixture, remove the vanilla pods, and gradually add the cornflour mix, stirring all the time. Bring to the boil once and remove the pan from the hob immediately. Pour the custard into glasses or bowls and serve lukewarm or cold, garnished with raspberries.

Serves 4

1 vanilla pod
500 ml full-fat milk
80 g erythritol
2 egg yolks
30 g cornflour
raspberries for garnish

Preparation time:
approx. 15 minutes
(plus cooking time)
Per portion:
approx. 151 kcal/632 kJ
6 g P, 8 g F, 14 g CH

STRAWBERRY
ice lollies

Serves 4

100 ml cream

150 g strawberries

3 tbsp erythritol

100 g creamy natural yoghurt

Preparation time:
approx. 15 minutes
(plus freezing time)
Per portion:
approx. 117 kcal/492 kJ
2 g P, 11 g F, 4 g CH

■ Whip the cream until stiff. Carefully wash and trim the strawberries and pat dry. In a bowl, mash them coarsely with a fork, then stir in the erythritol and yoghurt.

■ Fold in the cream and pour the mixture into 4 ice-lolly moulds (each approx. 75 ml). Put a stick in each one and freeze for at least 4 hours.

This delicious ice cream treat also tastes great made with raspberries or mango!

SWEET PANCAKES
with stewed apricots

Serves 4

For the stewed apricots:

250 g apricots

60 g erythritol

seeds of ½ vanilla pod

75 ml medium-dry white
   wine

For the pancakes:

4 eggs

6–8 tbsp erythritol

seeds of ½ vanilla pod

200 g almond flour

350 ml almond milk

30 g egg white powder,
   unflavoured

30 g raisins

1 pinch salt

You will also need:

40 g butter for frying

erythritol powder for
   dusting

■ For the stewed fruit: Wash the apricots, cut them in half, remove the stones, and quarter them. Bring them to the boil in a pan with the erythritol, vanilla seeds and white wine. Cook on a medium heat until the apricots are soft.

■ For the pancakes: Separate the eggs and whisk the whites until stiff peaks form. As you are doing this, gradually drizzle in the erythritol. Mix the egg yolks with the vanilla seeds. Add the almond flour, almond milk, egg white powder, raisins and salt, stirring well. Fold the stiff egg whites into the batter.

■ Melt half of the butter in a pan on medium heat. Pour half of the batter into the pan and cook until the underside is golden brown; carefully tear the pancake into pieces with two forks, turn the pieces over, and cook on this side until golden brown. Keep it warm and repeat the process with the rest of the batter. Dust with erythritol powder and serve with the stewed apricots.

Preparation time:
approx. 25 minutes
(plus cooking time)
Per portion:
approx. 553 kcal/2314 kJ
25 g P, 43 g F, 15 g CH

CHIA PUDDING
with strawberries

Serves 4
For the chia pudding:
600 ml almond milk
8 heaped tbsp chia seeds

For the topping:
2 oranges
400 g frozen strawberries
400 ml almond milk
120 g fresh strawberries
2 tbsp pine nuts

Preparation time:
approx. 15 minutes
(plus soaking time)
Per portion:
approx. 168 kcal/703 kJ
6 g P, 10 g F, 14 g CH

■ For the chia pudding: Into each glass, put 2 heaped tablespoons of chia seeds and 150 ml of almond milk, and leave this to soak overnight in the fridge. Stir well after 15 and 30 minutes to stop lumps from forming.

■ For the topping: Peel the oranges and chop the flesh coarsely. Whizz in a blender with the frozen strawberries and almond milk until you have a thick liquid. Divide it between the four glasses.

■ Wash the fresh strawberries, remove the stem ends, and cut them in half. Arrange the strawberry halves on top of the pudding and sprinkle with pine nuts. Serve immediately.

Chia seeds are a real superfood!
As far back as Mayan and Aztec
times, these power-packed
seeds were used as a source of
food and a healing agent.

BAVARIAN MOUSSE
with berries

Serves 4

3 sheets of gelatine
  (4.5 g powdered gelatine)

2 egg yolks

100 g erythritol

1 vanilla pod

200 ml milk

200 ml cream

berries of your choice

Preparation time:
approx. 25 minutes
(plus cooking and cooling time)
Per portion:
approx. 221 kcal/928 kJ
5 g P, 21 g F, 4 g CH

■ Soak the gelatine in water according to the instructions on the packet. Whip the egg yolks and erythritol until creamy. Cut the vanilla pod in half lengthways, scrape out the seeds, and put them both in a pan containing the milk. Bring them to the boil.

■ Prepare a bain-marie with moderately hot water and place the container with the egg yolks on it. Remove the vanilla pod from the milk and slowly pour the hot milk into the egg mix, stirring all the time. Continue to beat the mixture over a gentle heat until it becomes thick and creamy. Squeeze out the gelatine and stir it through the mixture.

■ Put the container with the mousse in a bowl of cold water and continue to beat until the mixture begins to set. Whisk the cream until stiff and fold it in. Transfer the mousse to a bowl and chill overnight. Serve by shaping the mousse into quenelles with 2 dessertspoons. Garnish with berries if you like.

PUMPKIN PUDDING
with coconut

Serves 4

800 ml coconut milk (tinned), chilled in the fridge

4 tbsp maple syrup

300 g pumpkin purée (tinned)

2 tbsp erythritol

1 tsp cinnamon

½ tsp ginger powder

1 pinch nutmeg

1 pinch salt

seeds of ½ vanilla pod

chopped pistachios for garnish

Preparation time:
approx. 15 minutes (plus chilling time)

Per portion:
approx. 130 kcal/543 kJ
2 g P, 10 g F, 8 g CH

■ Carefully open the coconut milk, without shaking the tin. Scoop off the thick layer of coconut cream and mix it with the maple syrup. Reserve 3 tablespoons of this mixture. Combine the rest with the pumpkin purée, erythritol, cinnamon, ginger powder, nutmeg and salt; spoon the mixture into glasses.

■ Mix the reserved coconut cream with the vanilla seeds and put a dollop on top of each pudding. Chill for at least 30 minutes. Serve sprinkled with chopped pistachios.

CHOCOLATE PUDDING
with peanut butter

Serves 4

½ avocado

4 tbsp unsweetened cocoa powder

3–4 tbsp erythritol

1 pinch salt

120 ml coconut milk

150 g smooth peanut butter

chopped peanuts for garnish

Preparation time:
approx. 15 minutes
Per portion:
approx. 303 kcal/1268 kJ
12 g P, 24 g F, 11 g CH

■ Cut the avocado in half and remove the stone. Scoop out the flesh and mash it well with a fork. Mix in the cocoa powder, erythritol, salt and coconut milk until the mixture is smooth and creamy.

■ Stir the peanut butter into the mixture, but do not work it in completely. Fill the glasses with the pudding and serve sprinkled with chopped peanuts.

ERYTHRITOL IS AVAILABLE IN HEALTH FOOD SHOPS OR ON THE INTERNET.

INDEX

INFORMATION

Abbreviations

CH = carbohydrate

cm = centimetre

F = fat

g = gram

kcal = kilocalorie

kg = kilogram

kJ = kilojoule

l = litre

ml = millilitre

P = protein

tbsp = tablespoon

tsp = teaspoon

Oven temperatures

The oven temperatures in this book apply to a standard electric oven. If you are using a fan-assisted oven, reduce the temperature by 20 °C. Unless otherwise indicated, the dishes are baked on the middle oven shelf.

Image credits

Recipe photos

pp. 3, 4, 14, 17, 22/23, 30, 35, 48, 60/61, 66, 84/85, 89, 93, 108/109, 112/113, 118, 122/123, 126/127, 135, 136/137, 144/145, 149, 152/153, 164, 167, 172/173, 175, 176/177, 179, 180/181, 184, 187, 188/189: Studio Klaus Arras; pp. 40, 114, 143: Kay Johannsen; p. 95: Lutz Jäkel; all others: TLC Fotostudio

Publicity images

pp. 7 and 12: © Daxiao Productions – Fotolia.com; pp. 18/19, 36/37, 54/55, 82/83, 104/105, 130/131, 156/157, 170/171: Studio Klaus Arras

Illustrations

Fotolia.com: p. 10 (top): © elenabsl; p. 11: © Oleh Tokarev; p. 15: © blueringmedia; p. 16: © volha; pp. 2, 5, 6, 8, 14, 6–17 (introduction border), 21, 27, 43, 46 (carrots), 67, 68, 87, 91, 94, 97, 125, 128, 134, 139, 142, 154, 168, 178, 186: © jente smiler; paper background: © tanawatpontchour; wood backgrounds: © merc67 and © homydesign; all others: © ~ Bitter ~

Text and recipes

Introduction, pp. 6–17: Christina Wiedemann

Recipes: pp. 40, 114, 143: Guido Gravelius; p. 95: Muriel Brunswig-Ibrahim; all others: VEMAG archives